THE BLEEDING LAND

Books by Giles A. Lutz:

THE HONYOCKER

THE LONG COLD WIND

THE GOLDEN LAND

THE BLEEDING LAND

Eli Dryden was bound and determined to stay out of the violent slavery dispute that raged the length and breadth of Kansas Territory in the 1850s. He paid no heed when his friends and neighbors insisted that he stand and be counted on the side of the abolitionists, for he had only one ambition: to work out a homestead claim and send home for the girl he loved.

Then his best friend was murdered by a pro-slavery hardcase, and Eli could no longer ignore the torment that scorched the land. He set himself on a personal vendetta that well suited the mood of "Bleeding Kansas" and eventually put his own life in the balance.

 LOOK FOR THE DOUBLE D BRAND

The Bleeding Land

GILES A LUTZ

Doubleday & Company, Inc.

Garden City, New York

1965

With the exception of actual historical personages,
the characters are entirely the product of the author's imagination
and have no relation to any person in real life.

.C.1

THE BLEEDING LAND

CHAPTER ONE

The late June day was hot, a reminder that even hotter days were in store for this country. Heat waves danced and shimmered along the riverbanks, and the slight breeze seemed too tired and listless to dispel them. The muddy water moved sluggishly, for the spring had been dry, and the tributaries of the Missouri River were dwindling. All along the river great stretches of bars were showing, the mica particles in the sand glistening like miniature gems under the baking sun. In ordinary weather most of those bars would be under as much as ten feet of water.

Eli Dryden leaned over the packet's rail, his eyes moving restlessly, going from the movement of the water to the movement of the river's wildlife above and on each side of it.

He didn't envy the *Emma Lou*'s pilot his job, and he imagined the price of growing old on this river was eternal vigilance. He saw the way the water split without apparent cause, running strong and divided for a long length before the two currents joined again. The water between the two currents moved at a different speed and course, rippling gently. His quick eyes saw the sand bar, lying just beneath the surface, the water covering it by scant inches. By tomorrow morning the bar would be showing. His respect for the river pilot's skill grew. This channel changed hourly, building and exposing new bars within a few hours' time. A pilot must not only locate those bars before he piled up on them, he must remember their location against his return trip.

A sudden boil in the water caught Eli's attention, then a log that had been submerged shot into view. Whatever had held the log had let go. It came off the bottom with a buoyant force that made it dangerous. Some of these logs were big enough to hole a boat's side, and even a lazy current could make a battering-ram of them. The pilot changed the wheel a few degrees, and the log slid harmlessly by.

Eli gave him an appreciative glance. He doubted that any of the other passengers had caught that deft bit of alertness and skill. He frowned at the two groups of them, clustered near the bow. All were going to Kansas Territory for the same purpose, but a distinct separation was between them as though a high wall separated them. And they hadn't as yet crossed the Kansas River. He saw their intent faces and their gesticulating hands as they talked. The separation between the groups had grown since St. Louis, and each group had tried to draw him into their quarrel. Few men were content to be able to do things their own way; they insisted that other men do it that way, too.

Eli smiled as he thought he hadn't been a popular man on this trip. But what other men thought of him concerned him not at all. He put his attention back on the river. He was no riverman, but he could see the fascination of it. This river was full of menace—hidden, shallow bars and half-submerged snags with fangs sharp enough to rip a boat's bottom from bow to stern. There was always something new in its ever-changing panorama that held a man's attention. Though he was a landlubber himself he could appreciate why another man liked an opposite thing.

The pilot rang a bell to claim the passengers' attention. "We'll raise Kansas City around the next bend," he called.

Eli heard the passengers' excited babbling, and for a moment the division between them was gone. Each man had a common goal—land. Kansas Territory had been opened, and people were determined to get their share of the new land. Kansas City was the doorway to that new land.

Eli shook his head. Opening land to people was like tossing a bone into the midst of a pack of half-starved dogs. He grinned as he thought, I'll do all the snarling and snapping necessary to get my taste of the bone.

There was almost contempt on the pilot's old, flinty face as he looked down on the passengers. Eli guessed that he had small liking for people. A dozen times he had heard the man snap an answer to some passenger's foolish question. The pilot had a crotchety, irritable manner, and he reminded Eli of his grandfather. He smiled as a piece of his grandfather's advice came into his mind. "Listen, look and learn," the old man had said. "You got eyes and ears, ain't you?" It was a sage piece of advice. A man could answer many of his own questions through observation.

His eyes were soft as he remembered his grandfather. He shifted his position at the rail. He was twenty-two years old, but he had a maturity beyond his years. He could thank old Eli for that. He had been named for his maternal grandfather, and his mother often had said despairingly, "You have all his bad traits. You're as stubborn as he is."

Eli admitted the stubbornness. But a man had a right to stay on the path he chose. He denied some of the other bad traits. Maybe old Eli had them, but he tried to make apology for them in his own manner.

There were mornings when old Eli had been touchier than a snake-bit hound dog, and Eli had learned at an early age to keep out of his way during those times. Once, old Eli had tried to make apology for his testiness. "Son," the old man had said, "no one wants to be so cussed mean. But there are times when it just wells up in a man, and it's got to come out. Old folks' bones ache a lot, and I guess we got to take it out on somebody. When I yell at you, will you forgive me?"

Eli had hugged him in an excess of love, and the old man turned his head and rubbed his eyes. "The damned dust," he growled. "If it's not one thing plaguing a man, it's another. Get along with you now. You think I want you pestering every step I take?"

Grandpa wanted. From that moment on, Eli knew it. Grandpa knew more than any man alive, and he had time to pass it on to younger ears. He knew where the papaws were and when they were ripe. He could look at the sky and tell

you what tomorrow's weather was going to be. He talked of
the wild critters and how watching them could teach a man.
His words rang in Eli's ears now. "When the ants march in a
straight line, depend on fair weather. But when they scatter
and run every whichway, keep your raincoat handy."

Eli hadn't seen an ant since he left Ohio. He was suddenly
horribly homesick for the sight of an ant. Old Eli died when
Eli was fourteen years old, and the loss would always be a
fresh, aching thing. He could still remember his rebellion
against God. Why did God take men like Grandpa and leave
other men who were no good to anyone? He had screamed
his defiance against God, and he had fully expected a lightning
bolt to cut through the clear sky and strike him. He had hid
to keep from going to the funeral, and his folks had been angry with him when they returned home. He had thought his
father was going to whip him, and he had shouted, "I don't
care. That wasn't Grandpa they were burying."

His words replaced his father's anger with wonder. "Boy,"
Cole Dryden said, "stop talking foolish." He was a big, plodding man, reticent with words and affection. The reticence
made him seem aloof, and a youngster was afraid to take his
problems to him.

Eli fought to keep the tears from spilling out of his eyes.
"It wasn't," he insisted. He had been shocked at the sight of
the little, frail man lying in the casket. That was a pitiful,
wasted man, and old Eli was a giant. "That wasn't Grandpa
in that box," he said.

Cole Dryden had a rare moment of understanding. He
dropped to his knees and drew his son to him. "You go ahead
and cry, Son. You're right. That wasn't the Grandpa we knew
at all."

Eli's feeling for his father changed from that moment on.
It wasn't that Cole was a bad father, only too tired most of
the time and filled with the impatience that goes with it.
How many dozens of times had Eli heard him say, "Don't
bother me now. Go ask your grandfather."

To some people maturity was years in coming, to a rare few

it was only stepping from one room to another. Eli took those few steps. From that day on, he understood his father. Cole Dryden was a hard-working man, beset with the problems of wresting a large family's living from a stubborn land. There was a span of years in a man's life that had to be given to hard, unremitting work, leaving little time for anything else. Old Eli had time for a boy, because he was beyond the span of those working years.

Eli had tried to tell his father he understood, but the words never came free. Each time he tried, they stuck in his throat. But he had tried to show him. Chores that he had ducked or performed with indifferent attention became debts of honor. He finished them in half the time he used to take and asked for additional work.

He remembered, when he was sixteen, his father had looked at him with puzzled eyes and asked, "What's gotten into you? You've changed almost overnight." He had whacked Eli on the shoulder and finished, "But I approve." It was the finest praise Eli had ever received.

Cole and Martha Dryden raised a large family. They had four sons and two daughters. If there was a shortage of anything while they were young, the kids didn't notice or mind. But as they grew older new instincts awakened, and new wants stirred. Mort was the first to be married, and Cole gave him forty acres of land. A man took a pride in seeing that his son got a start. Mort and his wife built and lived on that forty acres. There really wasn't much difference in Mort single and Mort married, except that the land had one more mouth to feed. Pardee married two years later. He, too, received forty acres of land. Eli remembered Pardee's wedding celebration. Cole had been a little drunk, but the whisky shine couldn't hide the worry in his eyes.

"You'll be next, Eli," Cole had said. "You know, I've been thinking about buying more land. What do you think about me buying that hundred and sixty of old Simmons?"

Cole Dryden was thinking of two more sons and two daughters to be married. That hundred and sixty acres was a fine thought, except that he couldn't possibly swing it. Two bad crop years had left him heavily in debt. Simmons might be willing to sell, but he wouldn't wait for his money.

Eli replenished his father's glass, then filled his own. Martha was frowning at them, but Eli didn't care. A man had a right to cut loose on his brother's wedding night.

"Don't you be worrying about giving me any forty acres, Pa. I'll never get married."

He had meant it at the moment. Then something happened a few months later that wiped the vow right out of his mind. He had literally bumped into Alicia Barnes. She had been coming out of Sloane's General Store, her arms laden with bundles, and he had walked into her. He heard her indignant cry as bundles flew every whichway. Both of them stooped at the same moment to retrieve a bundle, and they bumped heads.

She said, "Of all the clumsy—" Their eyes met, and her words faltered and died. It was really the first time he had looked into her eyes, and he had known her most of his life. He had never liked her. Her father owned more land than anybody in the county, and Alicia had always been that rich old Barnes kid. She rode a pony to school, where the other kids walked, and she wouldn't let any of them touch it. She was a spoiled, obnoxious, little snob, and there were times when Eli thought of using physical punishment on her.

She was eighteen, two years younger than Eli, when he bumped into her. Until that moment he couldn't have said what color her eyes were. He knew then. They were the color of a bluebird's wing, and they flashed like a bluebird's wings in flight. Her hair was a sunshine gold. Was it this curly when she went to school? He couldn't remember. There were other changes in her, changes that slammed a man's attention to a halt. He remembered her as a scrawny kid, all arms and legs. Time wrought some miraculous changes.

"It was my fault," he said. She would have to take his apology seriously. He could not stand it if the old scorn came back to her eyes.

"It was as much mine," she said, and laughed.

She had perfect teeth, and he wished he could make her laugh again.

He gathered up the bundles and carried them to the buggy. He helped her in and stood, looking at her. He wanted to say a hundred things, and his tongue was a stiff board. A faint color stole up the column of her throat, and a hope flooded him. Maybe she felt something, too.

"I was pretty awful in school, wasn't I, Eli?" The low notes of her laughter sounded again.

He gave it a moment's reflection. She was making some kind of an apology for those old days. A slow grin spread across his face. "Yes," he agreed. He let the shadow of a frown touch her face before he said, "And I was no better."

Her eyes turned clear and shimmering. She picked up the reins, and she seemed reluctant to go. "Will I see you again?"

She was tendering an invitation, and now if his tongue betrayed him again he would rip it out. "Tonight?" he asked hoarsely.

"I will be waiting," she said gravely.

He stood rooted until long after the dust from the buggy wheels had settled. A man was certain he knew the course his life was going to take. Then in the wink of an eye all the familiar landmarks were wiped away.

He had never thought much about his face until he shaved that evening. He wiped the remnants of lather away and scowled at the mirror. He must have been hiding when the looks were passed out. His ears were too big and his jaw was too square, giving a stubborn expression to his face. He could say the eyes were all right, well spaced and bright, but the black, bushy brows were as unruly as a wild plum thicket. His nose was crooked, the result of a schoolboy fight. He had a mobile mouth, the lips moving frequently with ready laughter. He was glad his teeth were straight and that none of them were missing. The wonder of Alicia Barnes, looking at him, filled him, and he shook his head. He couldn't complain about his size. He stood six feet two in his bare feet, and hard work

had muscled his frame and deepened his chest. His hand was
big enough to enclose a fair-sized cantaloupe. He pared and
cleaned his nails with care, frowning as he did so. Hard work
was evident in the broken nails and the calloused hands.

His younger brother, Timmy, plagued him all during his
dressing. "You're going to see a girl," Timmy said. "Why
else are you taking a bath in the middle of the week?"

Eli gave him a ferocious scowl. "You get out of here or I'll
swat you." He made a threatening move, and the fourteen-
year-old bolted for the door. Timmy stopped there, put his
thumbs in his ears, and waggled his fingers. Eli grinned at
him. He guessed being obnoxious was part of growing up.

He was unhappy about the threadbare condition of the
only suit he owned. He walked into the parlor, smiling self-
consciously.

Cole laid down the weekly newspaper and peered at him
over his glasses. "Well, look at the dude."

Martha's eyes gleamed with a sudden rush of excitement.
"It must be a girl, Eli."

He wanted to correct her. Not a girl. The girl. He tried to be
casual. "I thought I'd drop by to see Alicia Barnes."

His mother's face went still, and Eli knew a rush of anger
and disappointment. "What's wrong with her?" he demanded,
his feelings showing in his voice.

Martha rebuked him gently. "I didn't say anything was
wrong with her. She's a very beautiful girl." That was grudg-
ing praise. "I just don't want to see you hurt."

His voice stiffened. "I think I'm lucky."

Martha was wise enough not to push against his anger.

Cole spoke up hastily to break the strain between them.
"Do you want the wagon, Son?"

"I'm borrowing Pardee's mare."

Cole whistled. "You must have talked fast to get her."

Eli's grin returned. "I did. Pardee said if he found a hair
out of place, he'd skin me. Don't wait up for me."

He looked back from the doorway. For a moment he had

the foolish impression that some kind of entreaty was in his mother's face.

That first visit only confirmed what he already knew. Alicia Barnes was his woman. Six months after he started calling on her, he asked old Barnes for permission to marry her. Cyrus Barnes had never been happy about Alicia seeing Eli. He made it plain in a dozen ways, and his manner was a stone grinding away at Eli's temper. Eli never completely lost control. Perhaps Barnes hoped he would. Rage against her father might turn Alicia from Eli.

Barnes sat on the horsehair sofa, his weight making its springs sag. His fingers were laced across his paunch, and his eyes had a mean shine as he looked at Eli.

"It would be a good marriage for you, wouldn't it? You're not blind to all the advantages."

Eli's face burned, and that hard knot in his throat blocked his breathing. "I don't want anything from you." He managed to keep it just below a shout.

"You don't?" Barnes asked, and Eli had never heard more insult packed into two words. "Then how do you plan to support her?"

It was a big question. It lay in Eli's road like a rain-loosened boulder that had slipped from a cliffside. At the moment he could see no way of removing it. He could only say stubbornly, "I'll support her."

Cyrus Barnes was coldly amused. "When you can show me how, you can come back and ask me again."

Eli lay awake nights, prying at that boulder. When he married, Cole would try to give him forty acres. He could never accept it. The loss of another forty acres would cripple Cole. Besides, forty acres, even of the richest land, couldn't support a man and his family. He needed more land. But how was he going to get it? He tore at the problem until his thoughts were bruised. He took every extra job he could find, and his savings mounted with agonizing slowness. At this rate he would be a thousand years old before he could afford to buy the land he needed.

He heard about the news a week after it happened. May was his birth month, and President Pierce signed the Kansas-Nebraska bill at the end of May. It was almost like a birthday gift. The bill opened up virgin land to settlers. A man could have all the land he needed by driving a stake into the ground and scrawling his name on it.

He talked it over with Cole the day he heard about it. "People will be rushing out there like ants. And too many of them are closer to Kansas than I am. If I'm going to beat anybody, I've got to leave in the morning."

A heavy sigh underlay Cole's words. "I guess you've got to go, Son." Who could better understand the land hunger in a man? And who could also better understand how nearly impossible it was for a young man, without money, to satisfy that hunger around here? "Your ma's going to throw a fit. What does Alicia say about it?"

"I'll tell her tonight." Eli's eyes were worried. He would have to ask her to wait for him. If a woman loved a man, she would wait, but still, waiting was hard on a young girl. It was hard on a man. The thought of not seeing her for several months was like an open cut.

As they walked toward the house, Eli said, "Timmy will be needing land, too, one of these days. I'll try to claim enough land for all of us. The family will be together again out in Kansas."

"Maybe," Cole said. The word was empty. Once the ties of close association were cut, it seemed that everything worked against them ever being mended. He was right about Martha throwing a fit.

She argued with Eli; she used tears until Cole said sternly, "That's enough, Martha." It was hard enough for Eli without his mother pulling on him like this. "He knows what he has to do."

"But it's a savage land," she wailed. "Filled with Indians and wild beasts. I won't draw a free breath, worrying about what's happening to him." Tears welled in her eyes again, and she made a helpless gesture. "It's so far away."

Eli tried to make a joke to lighten her woebegone face. He got out the map and showed her where Kansas Territory lay. He put his forefinger on Ohio and his thumb on the territory. "It's not so far." He held up thumb and forefinger. "See. Less than two inches."

She gave him a tearful smile. One remaining hope was left to her. "Alicia won't let you go."

She was almost right. Alicia had cried, and Eli had taken her into his arms to console her. "You want us to be together for good, don't you?" he demanded. "This is the quickest way."

"I want us to be together now," she said rebelliously.

He kissed her eyelids, and his lips tasted the tears on her cheeks. He felt a new strength come into her fingers as they dug into his back. "I want to belong to you," she cried. "I want to belong to you now. I could wait then."

Ah God, how he wanted her. A man could bank a fire for only so long, then it went out or broke through.

A new demand was in her lips. He couldn't breathe because of their pressure, and he didn't care. The roaring in his head was the most beautiful music in the world. If she had asked him then not to go to Kansas, he would have given in to her.

Cyrus Barnes roared from an upstairs window, "Alicia, are you going to stay out there all night?"

She tried to draw Eli toward the copse of woods behind the house. She had a passion he had never suspected, and at the moment she would have defied anything.

"No," he said sharply. If he went with her, he gave up his plans. He could not leave her alone to face her father's wrath.

"One year," he promised. "As soon as I get the house built and the land broken, I'll come for you."

Barnes roared at them twice again before Eli could force her into the house.

Eli smiled ruefully as he thought that Barnes had been the only happy one to see him go. He had traveled three mighty rivers to get this far—the Ohio, the Mississippi and the Missouri.

The steamboat whistle and the passengers' yelling broke into his thoughts. His eyes had been wide and unseeing as he relived those moments. He had set himself a year, a year in which there would not be enough days or hours to do everything that must be done. But he had the incentive. He wanted her.

He looked toward the bridge. The pilot was pointing ahead. The boat was less than four hundred yards from the raw, little cluster of buildings at the foot of the bluffs. That was Kansas City.

Disappointment dampened Eli's eagerness. Kansas City was a misnomer. This handful of crude buildings was hardly in a village's class, let alone a city's. His face was grave as he picked up his worn and faded carpetbag and moved toward the gangplank. If Kansas City was the biggest settlement in this country, he was truly going to a raw and unsettled land.

CHAPTER TWO

Eli heard the familiar voice as he moved down the gangplank. He lengthened his stride, but there was no escaping Silas Tracy. The man had been a pest from the first day Eli set foot on the boat.

"Hold up there, Dryden," Tracy called. "Hold up, I say."

He came up puffing and took hold of Eli's arm. He was a short, fat man, red of face and short of breath. His round face was always moist, and his bulging eyes burned with a fanatic's zeal. Eli had deferred to him because of his age and calling, and that deference had cost him weary hours of listening. Silas Tracy was a preacher. He had left his flock in New England to fight the damnable slaveholders in Kansas. He was against sin in all its forms, but he would take any free drink offered him, and he talked constantly about resorting to violence—if need be.

He said excitedly, "Did you notice all those people who got on at St. Louis? All slavers. The slave states are rushing their people here."

Eli laughed. "How can you tell?"

Tracy frowned at him. "I can always pick out a slaver. It's time you made up your mind. You're either a free-state man, or a slaver. You can't stand on middle ground."

"I'm not standing on any ground," Eli snapped. He had come here with one purpose in mind, and some other man's purpose wasn't going to weaken or sidetrack him.

Something old Eli had said a long time ago came back to Eli. He had returned home after a fight at school, and his nose was still bleeding.

"In a fight?" old Eli asked.

Eli nodded. His nose hurt, and he was trying to keep the tears out of his eyes.

"Who with?"

"Jimmy Gardner."

"What did he do to you?"

"Nothing. I didn't want to fight him. The other boys pushed us into it."

He remembered the pressure of old Eli's hands on his shoulders. "You listen to me, boy. Don't ever fight because of somebody else's reasons. When you have to fight, be sure the reason is yours. Do you understand me?"

Eli understood, and he had never forgotten it. He remained silent, and Tracy tightened his hold on his arm. "Don't you know your not speaking up against them is helping them?"

"I told you I'm taking no part in politics."

Tracy looked horror-stricken. "Politics?" he echoed. "This is a matter of principle. Have you ever seen a slave?"

Eli had seen one. The black man had discreetly followed his master through the northern Ohio town, his eyes down, his steps soft. He was a matter of considerable curiosity in that small town. He was decently enough clothed, and he looked well fed.

Tracy said, "If you ever had, you'd feel differently. I've helped hundreds of them escape."

Eli doubted that. Tracy came from New Hampshire. New Hampshire was a long way from the slave states.

Tracy's eyes had the zealot's glow. "I'm here to help in seeing that Kansas does not come into the Union as a slaveholding state."

Eli thought a man like Tracy would hurt a cause more than he helped it. People rebelled instinctively against anyone who screamed at them, and Tracy was a screamer.

He said, "Excuse me," and removed Tracy's hand from his arm.

Tracy's face darkened. "I see you are against us. When you get into trouble, don't yell for us to help you."

Eli said curtly, "I take care of my own troubles."

He looked back after he descended the gangplank. Tracy was talking to a half-dozen men and pointing at Eli. Eli saw condemnation on the men's faces, and his anger stirred. Because he hadn't backed Tracy, Tracy was setting those men against him. He dismissed it from his mind. He would probably never see any of them again.

Kansas City's main street started at the river, ran a few blocks and died. The hot breeze stirred the foul air. The drying mud flats had their own offensive smell, mixed with the smell of men living together. Several gaunt dogs nosed around a garbage dump, ignoring the angry buzzing of hordes of disturbed flies.

The town was unpleasant to nose and eye. The buildings looked as though haste had been the prime consideration in erecting them. The lumber on many of them was still yellow-new from the sawing, and the sun pulled resin from the boards, collecting it in oozing bumps. The sun and the river air twisted and shrank the lumber, putting gaps between the boards. A man could pick out the older buildings by their deepening shades of weathered gray.

Eli squinted at the sun. It was beginning its slide into the western horizon. Kansas Territory lay only a few miles from Kansas City, but it might be best to stay here for the night. He didn't know what accommodations lay ahead of him, and he wasn't going to let haste stampede him into picking up the first open land he saw. He knew the kind of claim he wanted. The land must lay well, have good drainage and be somewhere in between upland and bottom land. Bottom land would be the more fertile. But a man could expect every so often to see his planting washed away by high water. Upland ground eliminated that worry, but in dry years the moisture went first from high ground, and crops suffered. He nodded in decision. He would stay here the night and try to find somebody who could advise him as to the best direction in which to start his search.

He passed a blacksmith's shop and a saddle maker. That square two-storied building a block ahead looked as though it might be a hotel, and he moved toward it.

A woman leaned against the doorway of a one-room house on his side of the street, watching him approach with speculative eyes. He had an impulse to cross the street to avoid her, then shrugged it away as childish.

She stepped out in front of him, and two of her upper teeth gave her smile a golden gleam. "Hello, dearie," she said.

He nodded politely and attempted to move around her.

She reached out and caught his sleeve. "What's your hurry, dearie?"

She was overpainted, and the strong sunlight was pitiless, revealing the tired lines in her face and the sagging flesh.

He knew why she had stopped him, and he couldn't keep the wash of color from his face.

She laughed at his reaction. The young men were the easiest of all to interest. Their eagerness wiped out any possible discrimination.

She asked, "Did you just get off the boat?"

He said curtly "Yes," hoping it would discourage her. Some of the boat's passengers stepped out into the street to go around them, and they gave him amused, knowing looks. He could throw her hand from his sleeve and push her out of the way, but he hated to be rude to any kind of a woman.

"Then you'll be looking for a hotel room?"

He nodded. She was taking a devious route to state what she had in mind.

"Stay with me, honey. It'll be almost as cheap, and you'll enjoy it a lot more."

The door to the house was open, and he saw the disorder inside. The bed looked as though it hadn't been made for weeks, and the mud-caked floor had probably lost all memory of a broom. A rank, animal odor came from her, the smell of a long-unwashed body.

He said "No," and swept her aside with an arm.

She cursed him. An oath matched every step he took, and they kept coming until he was almost out of earshot. As his embarrassment receded, he grinned. It looked as though one did not lightly reject a Missouri whore.

He walked into Gillis House, conscious of the sharp scrutiny he received from the men lolling in the lobby. The clerk was a bleary-eyed, bewhiskered man with the cause of his bleary-eyedness on his breath. He said, "You're pretty lucky, mister. We got one room left."

"How much?"

"Two dollars." The clerk saw the outrage forming on Eli's face and shrugged. The shrug said, take it or leave it.

Eli took it. His outrage grew as he saw the room. It was a dismal excuse for proper accommodations. The plank flooring was unswept, and the sheets on the bed were gray with dirt. The bed was the only item of furniture. The green blind at the window was tattered, and the breeze stirred the tatters, making a dry, rustling sound like far-off, derisive laughter.

One night, Eli told himself. One night's all I have to stay here. He asked, "Where's the water pitcher?"

The clerk cackled with laughter. "You're used to those fancy Eastern hotels, mister. We live rough out here. If you want to wash, go out in back like the others."

1

A tin basin was on a bench in the rear of the hotel. The last man who had used it hadn't emptied his wash water. The sides of the basin were coated with gray scum. The water bucket was empty, and Eli pumped a fresh one. He threw out the dirty water in the basin, rinsed it out, then refilled it with fresh water. He saw no soap and laved the water onto his face and hands. At least he could rinse away the dust.

He frowned at the towel hanging on a nail. An ant couldn't have found enough clean space to dry its whiskers. He pulled out his shirttail and patted his face and hands dry.

The clerk watched with evident relish. "You won't last long out here," he said. "Too damned particular. We've got some real rough men in this country. They'll swallow you without taking a long breath."

A pulse of anger throbbed in Eli's temple. He wanted to ask "Are you one of them," but he held back. Bandying words with this whisky wreck couldn't bring him the smallest of satisfactions.

He wanted to ask the location of a restaurant and decided against it. It would be best to steer clear of anything this man recommended.

He found a restaurant a block down the street. Its floor was covered with sawdust, but it hadn't been changed for a long time. The sawdust was matted and lumpy with caked mud and tobacco juice. A stale smell of old grease hung in the air. The appearance and smell of the place was warning enough, but he ignored it. He had his choice of six stools at the counter, and he sat down on the far one.

The man standing behind the counter was shirtless, and he kept itching at the armpits of his long-sleeved underwear.

"What'll it be?" he asked indifferently.

The choice was simple. Eli could have fried catfish and corn bread, or bacon and corn bread. He chose the catfish, figuring that with the river so near, the fish ought to be fresh.

The fish might have been fresh, but it was fried some time ago, and it was cold and soggy. It had also been fried in rancid grease, and Eli couldn't get the third bite down. The corn bread was grainy and as tasteless as compressed sawdust. A man's hunger faded quickly before such food.

His face didn't change as he paid the dollar the man requested. He knew one thing for certain. He wouldn't stay a minute longer in Missouri than was necessary.

He went back to his room and stretched out on the bed. He wanted to write to Alicia, but he found no paper in the room. He knew better than to ask the clerk for some. He had furnished the man enough laughs.

The room grew hotter and hotter. He could feel the sweat starting all over his body. The beads joined together and ran in little rivulets. He tried to keep his mind from the heat and discomfort. The more he tried, the more it bore down on him. He swore and got to his feet. He had no particular interest in any diversion the town might furnish, but anything would be better than lying here in this misery, even a walk along the river with its foul-smelling mud flats.

He walked through the lobby, and the clerk called something to him. Eli didn't turn his head. The sun was down, but the heat was still oppressive. It had a heavy, muggy quality, wrapping about a man like a hot, wet blanket.

The descending darkness was kind to this city, softening the square, harsh outlines of the buildings. Lamps were being lighted up and down the street, and the orange squares of light brought a recurrence of that horrible homesickness. This was always the best time of day. The work was done, and a man could relax, enjoying the talk and companionship with his family.

He heard a burst of laughter coming from the opened door of a building across the street. The place was better lighted than its neighbors, and as he glanced at it, two men entered it. He crossed the street to follow them into the saloon. He would buy a beer or two, listen to the talk, and perhaps gather a little information. Good fellowship usually prevailed in a tavern. Liquor swept away a man's natural suspicion of a stranger.

It was a raw, crude place, and the furniture was rough and

scarce. A bar ran the width of the room, and two tables and a few scattered chairs filled the small space before it.

A half-dozen men were in the room, and as Eli walked to the bar he was conscious of their scrutiny. He ordered beer and took his mug to a table. The beer was flat and warm. He sipped at it, his face impassive. The six men talked in low voices, and Eli could hear only an occasional word. He was the subject of conversation, for every now and then one of them turned his head for a look at him. Eli could feel the hostility in them flowing in tangible waves.

They were rough-looking characters. They were dressed alike except for the color of their shirts. Homespun trousers were stuffed into mud-caked boots, and the hafts of Bowie knives protruded from boot tops. Every man was armed, and two of them carried a brace of guns. Their shirts were red or blue with an insignia braided on breast and back. Eli saw three eagles, two hearts and an anchor. One of the men had a carbine swung over his shoulder, and two had swords dangling at their sides. All of them wore old slouched hats with a cockade or brass star on the front or side, and as an additional ornament, four of them wore a goose feather sticking in the band. Their hair was uncut and uncombed, reaching to their shoulders. None of them were shaven, and their hands and faces looked as if they hadn't washed for a week. All of them were hard drinkers. Glass after glass of whisky disappeared with amazing rapidity.

The whisky erased their caution, for a bearded giant roared, "By God, I ain't one to pussyfoot around. I went with Doniphan to Chihuahua, and we never took it by being careful. I say ask a man how he stands, and if he's against you, cut him down."

He received approving whacks on the back that would have floored a lesser man.

Eli felt a tightening run along his frame. Those men were drinking themselves up into some kind of a wrath, and it could easily turn on him. He wished he was out of here. He could jump to his feet and bolt for the door. He might make it, but he would not run. He drained the heavy glass mug and kept a grip on its handle. With enough force behind his swing, a man could turn the mug into an ugly weapon.

A voice said from the doorway, "You can start living now, boys. Sadie's here."

Eli turned his head. The woman who had accosted him on the street stood in the doorway. She wore a fresh dress, and the poor light from the three hanging kerosene lamps softened her make-up. This light was much kinder to her than sunlight. With the red shawl draped over one shoulder she looked fairly attractive.

The six men rushed her and swept her back to the bar, quarreling good-naturedly about who would buy her a drink.

Eli let out his breath. Sadie's appearance took the men's attention from him.

Sadie could drink with them. She downed three glasses of whisky in rapid succession, and the giant said, "Sadie, you must be hollow all the way down." He roared with laughter and threw his arm about her. He jerked her to him and Sadie cried, "Be careful, you big ape. This is a new dress." She gave him a bright, false smile, softening her rebuke. "You keep buying them, Tim, and I'll keep drinking them."

Tim grinned. "And I'll collect for the drinks later."

She tapped him lightly on the cheek. "And that will cost you, too."

She turned her attention to the rest of them and pulled a single-sheet newspaper from beneath her arm. "Are you boys planning on going into Kansas tomorrow?"

"Tomorrow or the next day," Tim said carelessly. "There's no rush."

"There might be," she said. "The paper says the blue-bellies are rushing here from every Northern state. All the land might be gone before you decide to move."

"We took Chihauhua," Tim said. "You don't think Kansas will be as hard as that?"

"Senator Atchison thinks it might be," she answered. She

spread the paper on the bar. "He's written about it in the *Argus*."

"Read it to us, Sadie," one of the other men said.

Sadie enjoyed her moment of importance, and Eli suspected none of the men could read. She read poorly, fumbling and halting over some of the words. "Will you bordermen let the abolitionists take the land that so rightfully belongs to you? I say stake out claims immediately and woe be to the abolitionist or Mormon who shall intrude upon it, or come within reach of your long and true rifles, or within point-blank shot of your revolvers." She raised her head and looked at them. "That's what he says," she said triumphantly.

"He writes real good," one of the men said. The whisky and Sadie's reading inflamed him. "By God, no blue-belly better set foot on my claim."

Eli decided he could slip out now. He pushed his chair from the table and stood. He picked the wrong moment. The chair legs screeched over the uneven flooring. The sound pulled heads toward him.

Sadie looked at him with bright-eyed malevolence. "I'll bet he's one of them. He's too good to talk to common folks like us."

"Maybe I'd better find out." Tim drained his glass and set it down. He wiped his mouth with the back of his hand and moved with ponderous, slightly unsteady steps toward Eli.

Eli gripped the mug again.

Tim stopped within three feet of him. His jaw was thrust forward, and an ugly look rode his face. "How do you sound on the goose?" he demanded.

Eli glanced at the feather in the band of the hat. Evidently, it meant more than just an ornament. His smile was strained. "I'm sorry, but I don't know what you mean." He thought a newcomer had just come in, but he didn't dare turn his head.

"He's not one of us, Tim," somebody yelled.

"Goddamit," Tim roared, "don't you think I can see that?" He looked at Eli again. "So you came here thinking you could steal our land."

"I'm stealing nobody's land," Eli said in a tight voice. "I've got as much right to claim land as anybody."

"Maybe you'll get that idea stomped out of your head," Tim said.

His fists were balled, and Eli watched his eyes. He saw the intention in them before Tim started the step. He took a long stride, swinging the mug as he moved. He aimed for that out-thrust chin and his forward momentum gave the swinging mug a terrible force. He was outweighed by a good forty pounds. He had to have that first blow.

His aim was perfect. The bottom of the mug smashed against the point of the big man's chin and broke, leaving the handle in Eli's hand. Tim swayed, and his eyes turned glassy. He tried to reach Eli, but his knees unhinged, throwing him off course. He took a lurching step to one side, his hands paw-ing futilely before him. He had tremendous vitality. That blow should have dropped a steer, and he was still on his feet.

He came apart all at once, falling heavily on his face. His head rose, then fell back. A quiver ran through him, and he was out.

A silence hung in the room, heavy with the import of the unusual. None of these men had ever seen Tim in this posi-tion. Their faces were awed as they looked from Tim to Eli.

Sadie broke the silence. "Are you going to let him do that to Tim?" she screeched.

Her demand goaded them into action. They spread out in a half arc, moving slowly at Eli. He cast a trapped glance to-ward the door. The man at the north end of the arc had a shorter angle to the door than he did. If he made a sudden break for the door, he might catch them by surprise. But he also would be turning his back to them. He saw their faces, ugly with intent. If he turned his back, he would be swarmed under. Once they put him on the floor, he would never get to his feet. They would kick and stomp him to death. He might have made his break at the exact moment Tim was sagging, when all eyes were on Tim. But that moment was gone. He had been as fascinated as the others, watching Tim fall.

He knew how a treed tomcat felt with a pack of angry dogs yapping away at the base of the tree. But the cat had a tremendous advantage over Eli. The dogs couldn't get to the cat. These men could get to him.

He retreated a step and seized a chair by its back. He lifted it and knew a sudden excess of anger. "Come on," he yelled. "I'll break your goddamed heads."

The raw savagery in his face put caution in them, but it didn't stop them. They slowed their steps and spread out a little farther. But they kept coming.

He backed until he had the solid feel of a wall against his shoulder blades. At least none of them could slip up on him from the rear. He held the chair, ready to swing it at the first man who came within reach. If he were lucky, he might get two of them. And that depended upon too many imponderables. It depended upon how fast he moved, if he could keep his feet under him, if the chair held together, if they got in each other's way. If he were extremely lucky, he might get the third one. But that would still leave two on their feet. The odds were impossible.

They advanced in a slow, semi-crouch, a naked hunger for violence in their eyes. Eli drew a deep breath and tightened his grip on the chair.

A voice from the doorway said, "That's far enough." It contained crisp authority. It stopped the five men and pulled their heads toward it.

Eli's eyes swung to the doorway. A man stood there, holding a small Colt. The angles and planes of his face were sharply hewn, and in the poor light his cheeks looked hollow. His nose was his most prominent feature, hooked like the predatory beaks of birds of prey. His eyes were bright and flashing, and they held the room with an odd power. He was dressed in black broadcloth, and his linen was crisp and fresh. He was not six feet tall, but he gave the appearance of greater height by the straightness of his stature and the leanness of his frame.

The five men were armed, and the small Colt couldn't possibly stop all of them. Violence was a hungry rodent nibbling at the people in the room with its sharp rat teeth. The stranger had to be aware of the explosiveness of the moment, yet nothing showed in his face.

One of the five made a tentative move, and the lean man said, "I'll put a bullet in you." His manner was more forceful than his words, and he jerked his hand from his waist.

"Disarm yourselves," the newcomer said. White teeth flashed in a cold smile. "Careful. Or I'll spill your blood."

This was the moment that hung in abeyance, when it teetered on the razor-sharp edge of crisis. The slightest move could topple it either way. If the concentrated rebellion at the order was stronger than the lone authority—Eli held his breath.

One of the men's hands moved slowly to the buckle of his pistol belt. His fingers fumbled at the tongue, and the belt opened and fell to the floor.

"Very good," the stranger said. "Kick it in the corner."

He nodded approvingly at the kick that sent the belt skittering across the floor.

Eli let out that breath. He felt weak and hollow inside. The moment of crisis was gone, and it left a favorable reaction for the man in the doorway. And for myself, he thought.

Other weapons fell to the floor and were kicked across it. Men glowered and swore, but there was no danger in words or looks.

"Would you care to leave your new-found friends?" the lean man asked Eli.

Eli realized he still held the chair over his shoulder. His arms were trembling, and an ache was stealing along them. He set the chair down and moved toward the doorway. His legs had picked up a weakness. He had to force them to move.

The man stepped aside, and Eli walked past him out into the night air. He heard the man say, "I wouldn't follow us. I haven't killed my man for the day, yet."

He moved deliberately from the doorway toward Eli. But once darkness cloaked him he broke into a run. Eli didn't have to be told to follow him.

They pounded down the street for half a block, then cut between two buildings. They came out behind them and veered sharply to the right. Eli's lungs were pounding when his benefactor halted suddenly. He started to say something, and an upflung hand stopped him. The man's head was cocked in a listening attitude.

Eli listened, too, and heard no outbreak from behind them.

The man said, "It'll take them a few minutes to gather and sort their weapons. And they will want to revive Tim. Tim would hate to miss the search for us. Are you staying in town?"

Eli's breathing was leveling. "At Gillis House."

"I'd advise you to move. I'm camped out of town about a mile. I'd be happy to have you join me."

"Can I get my bag?"

"If we hurry."

Eli said, "I'm Eli Dryden," and thrust out his hand.

Strong, white teeth flashed in a smile. "Jim Lane. I am delighted to know you." Lane's handclasp was firm.

Eli said, "You saved my life."

"Maybe," Lane said carelessly. The smile flashed again. "I won't hold it over your head. I'd suggest we don't delay too long."

He turned and moved with rapid strides, and Eli followed him.

CHAPTER THREE

Eli got his bag and came down into the lobby. Something awakened the dozing clerk, and he jerked to dull, blinking attention.

He saw the carpetbag in Eli's hand, and a quick belligerence swept the dullness away. "So we're not good enough for you? Don't expect your money back."

"I want to keep the room," Eli said gravely. "I'm expecting some friends. Send them right up." He wished he could see the rage on Tim's face when he looked into the empty room.

He walked outside, and Lane asked, "Do you have a gun in that bag?"

Eli shook his head.

"I'd advise you to buy one as soon as you can. This way." He led off into the darkness.

Eli caught up with him. His legs were longer than Lane's and he could have moved at a faster gait. He heard yelling and turned his head. The yelling sounded two or three blocks away and, while dulled by distance, it still contained an angry note.

"That's probably Tim," Lane said dryly. "He's got a voice to match his size. He'll tear the town apart looking for you. Tim Copple is a vindictive man."

"I'll be just as happy not to see him again."

Lane said sharply, "Kansas is a big, empty land. But don't plan on not running into him again. Time won't dull his memory. Make no mistake about that. If you see him again, the best thing to do is to shoot him on sight."

Eli didn't take the warning lightly, but he wasn't going to carry it around with him. That kind of a burden grew heavier every day.

They walked in silence, and after fifteen minutes Eli looked behind him. The lights of the city were swallowed in the empty blackness. The sky was moonless, and the stars were dim and subdued.

"A new moon about midnight," Lane said. "Watch your step. It's rough ground."

Eli stepped into a depression and grunted as the jolt ran through his body. Some kind of heavy grass pulled at his boots and slowed his steps. Lane appeared to know where he was going, and Eli moved with him in silence. It seemed as if an hour had passed, but it couldn't have been over twenty minutes, when Lane said, "In here. Watch for low branches." He stooped as he entered a grove of small, black-walnut trees.

In places the young trees grew so closely together a man could not pass between them. A branch scraped Eli's cheek, and he started at its touch.

"We're here," Lane said, and stopped. His night vision must have been excellent, for Eli could see nothing. He started more violently at the soft, blubbery snort, sounding a few yards ahead of him.

"Somebody's here," he said tensely.

"My horse." There was amusement in Lane's voice. "I wouldn't dare take him into town. My sympathies are too well known. Somebody would steal him."

Eli's vision adjusted to the darkness. He saw Lane stoop over and heard the dry, rustling sound as Lane wiped a match into life against his pants leg. He touched it to a prepared fire, and the dry leaves and small sticks caught and flamed into larger life. The flames lapped hungrily at thicker sticks, and for a few moments, the growing fire was dazzlingly brilliant. Eli's eyes made another adjustment. He saw a bedroll and a few utensils near the fire.

"Won't the fire be seen?" He couldn't quite hide the worry in his voice.

Lane shook his head. "Unlikely. I've already camped here three nights. We're quite a way out of town, and the grove is thick. I've got coffee in my saddlebags. Will you join me in a cup?"

Eli nodded. He needed a cup of coffee.

Lane poured water from a canteen into a blackened pot. "It's river water and tastes of mud. But the coffee will kill the taste." He placed the pot on the flames and looked at Eli. "Were you afraid back there?"

A rueful grin touched Eli's face. "They had me cut off from the door. Couldn't you hear my knees knocking?"

"An honest man admits his fear. I saw you hit Copple. It was a good blow."

"The woman set them on me. I guess I insulted her by not going into her house."

Lane smiled. "Sadie doesn't realize her favors are dimming."

"Copple asked me a question. When I couldn't answer it, he was ready to jump me. I didn't even know what he meant."

"What did he ask you?"

"How do you sound on the goose. Does that make sense to you?"

"It's one of their passwords." Lane shook his head. "The bordermen are like children. But very dangerous children. They judge a man's sympathy to them by his soundness on the goose. I don't know where or how it started. I doubt they do. But it gives them a chance to stick a feather in their hat and strut about. Men like ex-senator Atchison play on their ignorance. If he can throw a flaming issue into their faces, they'll support him against Benton, and he'll go back to the Senate. He has his issue in whether Kansas will be admitted as a slave or a free state."

He shook the pot, and the beginning of a boil sounded from it. "If you had been sound on the goose, you would have been a slaver. You would have been one of them."

"I never owned a slave in my life. Neither did my family. I came here to claim land. And for no other reason."

"They won't let you stay out of it. One side or the other will draw you in." Those intense eyes bored into him. "You are against slavery, aren't you?"

"I'm against it. But I'm not fighting another man because he owns slaves. If he lets me alone, I'll let him alone."

Lane stared into the flames. "It won't be as simple as that. The issue of Kansas coming into the Union as a free or slave state is a political beanbag. The South must have Kansas as a slaveholding state, or lose all chance of regaining political equality. California came in as a free state, and that gave the North sixteen states to the South's fifteen. The South has no territory into which to expand. You see Missouri was admitted as a slave state in 1820 only on the South's agreement that any other new states carved out of territory above the 36-30

parallel would be free. The 36-30 parallel is Missouri's southern border."

A hard boil sounded from the coffeepot, and the aroma of
coffee drifted in the air.

Lane lifted the pot from the fire. "It's ready. I am sorry, sir,
I can offer you no sugar or cream."

"I take it black, Mr. Lane."

Lane flashed him a smile. "Jim to my friends." He poured
two tin cupfuls and handed one to Eli. "It's hot," he warned.

The heat ran into the handle of the cup, and Eli shifted
it from hand to hand. He sipped at it gingerly. It was scalding
hot and strong enough to pull a wagon, but it tasted good
to him.

Lane gave him a rueful smile. "But I bore you. A man
forgets that things that stir him do not touch another."

"No," Eli said. "I'd like to know more." He thought that
Lane should have been a politician. He had a command of
English and a beautiful voice. It was easy for a man to become
enthralled listening to him.

"Our lawmakers get themselves into one mess after another. They let New Mexico and Utah come into the Union
with the settlers having the right to decide if they would be
a slave state or free. The settlers wrote squatter sovereignty
into law. It had to apply when Kansas Territory was opened.
The side that gets here first with the most people will win."

"Which side will that be?"

"The North, if I can help it." A burning passion was in
Lane's voice. "I look at it as a moral issue, rather than a
political one. Tim Copple is an example of the kind of man
I'm fighting."

Eli nodded. That wasn't hard to understand.

"I can also understand Missouri's position. She has fifty
thousand slaves in her border counties. Thirty million dollars
invested in human flesh. She cannot afford to have a free
state as her western neighbor. So Atchison stirs up the border
ruffians. They will use terror and violence to drive out men

with free-state sympathies. They want as few free-state men here as possible, when the time comes to vote."

"And the North is doing nothing about it?"

"Oh yes. The Massachusetts state legislature gave a charter to an aid society. It's said this aid society will raise five million dollars to send twenty thousand settlers into Kansas." Lane replenished his cup and proffered the pot to Eli.

Eli shook his head. His cup was more than half full. He had been too engrossed in listening to Lane to drink his coffee.

"The figures are probably exaggerated," Lane said. "But the society stands to make a great deal of money. It will send in grist mills and steam sawmills. That will cost, but they'll more than get it back. Company agents are already on the ground taking up sections of land on which boardinghouses and mills will be located. They will wind up with many reservations of six hundred and forty acres of valuable land. Oh yes, the society wants to see Kansas come in as a free state."

He drained his cup and threw the grounds over his shoulder. "Eli, no man moves without a selfish motive."

"Do you?" Eli's question was challenging.

Lane chuckled. "Ten years ago, the answer would have been 'no.' Today, I can truthfully say I want nothing but to claim my land and be allowed to live on it in peace."

"That's all I want."

Those eyes pierced Eli again. "But will you fight for that privilege?"

It always came back to that question, and Eli said irritably, "Silas Tracy kept asking me that on the boat."

Lane nodded. "I know him. He has been in here before. He is a loose-mouthed fool. He will find the cloth and his age will not protect him."

He saw the question in Eli's eyes and smiled. "I know all of the prominent people concerned in this. A man knows the ground he walks on, or steps in a hole."

"Can't men of different opinion live together without fighting?"

Lane sighed. "Not yet, Eli. Maybe never. In the meantime, the best we can do is to protect ourselves."

He held out the coffeepot, and Eli shook his head.

Lane said, "We left a lot of it. It'll do to warm over in the morning." He set the pot on the ground beside the fire and walked to the bedroll. He came back with a blanket.

He handed it to Eli. "It might soften the ground a little."

Eli thanked him and spread the doubled blanket on the ground. He stretched out on it, his clasped hands behind his head.

Lane squatted on his heels, several feet from the fire. He stared into it, and Eli wondered what he saw.

"Aren't you going to bed?" If Lane felt sentry duty was necessary, Eli wanted to take his share.

"In a few minutes." Lane filled a pipe, picked a burning stick out of the fire, and lit the tobacco. The flame, close to his face, highlighted it. It put shadowy hollows in his cheeks and made his cheekbones stand out more prominently. It picked up the bright, almost fanatical gleam in his eyes.

Eli thought, here was a man who could command almost any situation, and he felt a fumbling inadequateness around him. He said gruffly, "I am grateful for tonight."

Lane turned his face slowly toward him. Now his features were in shadow. "You don't have to be. Don't feel you're in my debt."

Eli felt some sort of urgency hemming him in. A man planned his life, then things happened that ripped those plans to shreds. He said, "All I want is to stake out a claim for myself and maybe for my brothers and father. Is that asking too much?"

Lane said gravely, "It could be asking too much."

The last thing Eli saw before he went to sleep was Lane staring into the fire.

CHAPTER FOUR

Lane was the first awake in the morning. He tugged on his boots, stretched and yawned, then glanced toward Eli. Eli was still asleep, and the early sun coming through the leaves dappled his face. It wasn't a handsome face in any sense, but it was a strong one. Lane could still see him standing against the wall, gripping that chair. He would have broken a couple of heads before they swarmed him under. Eli admitted the fear that was in him, and that pleased Lane. Only a coward bragged he was never afraid, and that was done when the time and event were of no importance. Lane was pleased with his encounter with Eli. Lane had told him that he was in no debt to him, but the debt was there, nonetheless. Honesty stuck out all over this young man. The debt would be repaid at the first demand.

Lane moved softly about the campsite, gathering fresh fuel for the morning fire. He would not break the sticks, lest the noise awake the sleeping man. He liked this time of day, when the air was clean and fresh, when the hours were not yet old enough to pile their wearying burden on a man.

He envied Eli his youth, though he didn't feel old. Forty was not old. It was a point he argued frequently with himself. Dwelling on past mistakes and failures was the thing that aged a man, and he would not permit them to enter his mind. This time there would be no mistake, no failure. This whole, vast land lay before him, ready for the taking.

Eli frowned as the sunlight strengthened, and Lane thought it would awaken him. Instead, Eli threw his arm across his eyes. Eli Dryden was the kind of a man Lane wanted. He was young and tough, and those were the qualities Lane needed. Eli was a sharp tool, to be used, then cast aside before that edge turned in Lane's hand. Give him a hundred young men,

men who believed in him, and he could take Kansas. The goal was bright and shining. When Kansas was admitted into the Union as a state, Jim Lane would be her first governor.

The moral issue bothered him not at all. He would as soon buy or sell a nigger as he would a mule. He picked the Northern viewpoint because it was the stronger. In the long run the North would pour more settlers into Kansas and so control it. A smart man chose the winning side and became one of its leaders. Then when things settled down, its leaders were re-membered by a grateful people.

He poured more water and coffee grounds into the pot and set it on the fire. It was going to be a meager breakfast. He had had to run with Dryden last night before he bought his supplies.

He looked at Eli again. He would let him sleep until the coffee boiled. Dryden was a stubborn, determined man, but he would change his mind—or more likely, it would be changed for him. Lane foresaw the coming conflict. Differences of opinion would flare into open violence. Kansas would be lucky if the violence could be stopped short of civil war. He felt no distress at the thought. A man could not stop the happening of events. The best he could do was to take their aftermath and shape it to his own aims. Eli Dryden might be stubborn today. Tomorrow, the stubbornness would weaken. Self-preservation had a way of watering down the loftiest of ideals. Dryden would join with the other settlers of similiar viewpoint—or he would perish.

The sound of the boiling coffee awakened Eli. His eyes flew open, and there was no sleep fog in them. He awakened like an animal—instantly and alert.

Lane thought, It's a quality that will stand him well here. He said, "Good morning. The best I can offer you is coffee."

"That will be fine." Eli pulled on his boots and stood. He stretched and yawned. "We don't dare go into town for break-fast?"

"That would be foolhardy. Tim Copple holds his anger and whisky equally well."

Eli grinned and took up a notch in his belt. "I've missed breakfast before."

Not often, Lane thought. Dryden had that well-cared-for look that came from being part of a family that cared. He felt almost an anger at Dryden and turned his head lest it show in his eyes.

He poured two cups of coffee and said, "I'm going into Kansas today. You're welcome to go with me."

Eagerness flooded Eli's face, and he forgot his coffee. "I've been hoping to run across somebody who knew the land." He wanted their association to grow. He respected this man. It could easily grow into deep liking.

"We'll stay away from Leavenworth, Kickapoo and Atchison," Lane said. "They're on the west bank of the Missouri, closest to the border. Bordermen were slipping across the river before President Pierce signed the bill into law. They've grabbed the nearest choice land. Those three towns are their strongholds."

He saw the disappointment in Eli's face and said, "There is as good land elsewhere." His gesture took in half of the compass. "Anywhere a man looks, he can find land to satisfy his most exacting standards. I know of one piece that would be just right for you."

A subtle stiffening touched Eli's face. "I'd have to see it first."

Lane nodded and gave him an easy smile. "You will. We can ride double until the mare tires."

Eli demurred, and Lane said, "You'll be grateful enough for her legs before the day's out."

Eli liked the mare the moment he saw her. She had the long, slender legs that denoted speed. She was a deep bay with a blaze running from forelock to muzzle. Her coat showed lack of care, for some of the mud cakes in it were old. Eli excused it. Lane probably didn't have the time to spend on her.

She snorted at Eli's approach, and her ears twitched. He extended a hand slowly, and she reached out and nuzzled it.

"She's usually slow to make up with strangers," Lane said. "You have a way with animals."

Eli grinned. "I like them." He would have to buy a horse. But he wouldn't be able to afford an animal this fine.

He insisted upon walking, for a while anyway, and Lane couldn't change his mind. This was more of that stubbornness, and Lane said with a tinge of exasperation, "At least give me your bag."

Eli handed it up, and Lane secured it behind the saddle. "We'll avoid the ferry at Kansas City. It's usually crowded. And Copple could be watching it. We'll go in through Westport."

Eli nodded. He knew nothing about the country. He depended upon Lane, and whatever Lane said was fine with Eli.

Lane moved the mare out at a slow walk, and Eli strode beside it. Lane made an impressive figure on horseback. He sat a horse well, and the mare responded to the authority in his hands.

After a mile Lane offered to change places, and Eli refused. "Then climb up here for a way," Lane said. "She can take it."

Eli shook his head. "I'm enjoying it." The morning was not yet warm enough to make walking an effort. He was used to walking, and he liked it. He could walk all day and feel no more than a normal weariness.

A nerve jumped in Lane's cheek, and he stared straight ahead. He rode for a while in silence, then said, "Perhaps we can find you a horse in Westport."

Eli nodded cautiously. Buying a horse depended upon at least two things—his approval of it and the price.

He said, "This road is well traveled." Countless wheels and hoofs had cut through the tough prairie sod and beaten out a packed road. Heavy wagons had plowed through this road in muddy times, and their deep tracks had hardened. It would take years to efface those ruts.

Lane's face relaxed. "Westport is exactly what it says. The port of the West. A great road leads out of it. It forks after a few miles into the territory. The right-hand fork is the Cali-

fornia road. It heads north and joins the Oregon Trail. The
left-hand road goes to Santa Fe. Majors and Russell have
made a fortune out of that road, freighting merchandise to
Santa Fe. At one time they had seven thousand oxen and
mules and hired a thousand bullwhackers to drive them. But
the profits are diminishing. If they hang on long enough,
they'll go broke."

That touch of awe was back in Eli's voice. "Is there anything you don't know about this country?"

Lane's good humor was restored, and he chuckled. "I made
it my business to learn all I could about it."

"And I'm glad to be with you."

Lane nodded at the sincerity in Eli's voice. His one great
fault was his impatience with another man's viewpoint. He
had never really learned to curb it.

He said, "A couple of miles will bring us into Westport.
We can buy food there. Sure you won't ride?"

This time Eli's refusal didn't touch him.

Eli liked this country. He took into account that he was
seeing it at the height of the growing season, and no country
suffered from that. It was grassland, laced with timber along
the creek bottoms. Walnut, hickory, elm and oak marked the
meandering courses of the streams. He saw cottonwoods he
couldn't encircle with the stretch of his arms, and the drooping gracefulness of willow trees fought for growing space
against their larger relatives. In the bottoms the wild grass
grew almost as tall as his head, and the air was filled with the
fragrance of elderberry, gooseberry, plum and mandrake blossoms. Quail and prairie chickens were constantly jumping up
from either side of the road, and on a nearby ridge he caught
a glimpse of a flock of wild turkeys.

He said, "A man could live off this country."

"He could," Lane agreed. "Though the buffalo and deer
have moved on farther west. It's a fertile land. In a few years
hundreds of people will walk where only one walked before."

His words put a rush of impatience in Eli. He wanted to
crumble land in his hand—his land.

Lane said, "There's a good spring around the next bend. We'll stop for a while."

The clear spring gushed from a rocky ravine. It flowed a good six inches wide, gurgling as it ran down through the rocks. Eli stared at it with appreciation. If it ran this much of a flow during dry weather, it probably ran the year around. With a spring like this on his place, a man would never have to worry about water for his stock. He made a mental note. He wanted a spring like this.

"I can dig out a cup," Lane offered.

Eli shook his head. It was sacrilege to use a cup on a spring like this.

He lay on his belly and thrust his face into the water. It ran clear and cold, and its tingle put renewed vitality into one. A man could not satisfy his thirst at once. The water was too cold against his teeth.

He slaked his thirst and raised his head. "It's still the best drink ever made."

Lane smiled at him. "You're just missing the mud taste of Kansas City water."

Eli returned the smile. It was a shared, full moment, and he felt very close to Lane.

Lane led the mare a few feet down the ravine and let her drink. She expressed her pleasure in soft snorts, and the drops of water, falling from her muzzle, shone like small jewels in the sunlight.

Lane straightened from his drinking. "I'm really hungry now. We'll eat when we reach Westport. You ride the rest of the way."

"No," Eli said flatly. Lane owned the horse. Somehow, it didn't seem proper that Lane should have to walk into Westport.

Lane shook his head. "You are a stubborn man." This time he could say it without a trace of stiffness.

Westport, Missouri, was bigger than Kansas City. Two things about it struck Eli immediately. It was cleaner than Kansas City, and the smell of the mud flats was missing.

The streets were crowded with traffic, and Lane said, "Westport is an important supply center. Both for Kansas and the Southwest. Most of the people around here are pro-slavery. Don't talk against it."

Eli said dryly, "I didn't intend to."

Lane gave him a brief, piercing glance, then put the mare into a brisk walk.

Eli saw him stop before a small building a block away, dismount and tie the mare. The way Lane moved off showed that he was displeased at what Eli had said.

Lane was inside the building by the time Eli reached it. He walked into the little room, and the appetizing aroma of properly prepared food filled his nostrils. Lane was seated at a table, his face set in a brooding look.

Eli sat down, and Lane said, "I don't understand you. I give you the best advice I can, and you take it lightly."

"I didn't take it lightly. I had no intention of talking for or against it."

Lane's laugh was brittle. "You are a determined young man." Then his face cleared and he said, "I'm getting cantankerous with age. Forgive me."

"Nothing to forgive," Eli said, and forgot it.

A pleasant-faced woman waited on them. Her plumpness showed an ample intake of good food. Her hair was graying, and she reminded Eli of his mother. Homesickness washed over him, and he wondered if its force would ever diminish. She said, "I can give you stewed chicken and dumplings." Lane nodded. "Perfect."

As she moved away Eli called after her, "Make the portions big."

She brought him a heaping plate, and he sat for a moment, savoring its appetizing aroma. He took his first bite. This woman was a cook. The dumplings were light, and the chicken was cooked to a turn and flavored properly.

Lane finished eating long before Eli did. He watched Eli finish his second plate and said, "Where do you put it? If I eat too much, it shows up on me tomorrow."

Eli pushed back his plate and sighed with repletion. He grinned at Lane. "That's the first decent meal I've had since I left Ohio."

"Keep it in mind. The memory of it may have to last you a long time." It was a subtle warning that the land ahead was not as civilized as Westport, Missouri.

Eli reached into his pocket to pay the woman, and Lane said, "I've already paid her."

Eli frowned. Lane must have paid her when he got up and walked to the counter for an instant. He tried to repay Lane, and Lane refused. He slapped Eli on the back and said, "What are we doing, arguing over a meal? It was my pleasure."

The frown remained on Eli's face as he followed Lane outside. Sometimes a man couldn't help being in another's debt, but there was no sense in that debt mounting up when it could be avoided.

Lane said, "Meet me here in thirty minutes." His eyes shone as though some inner secret pleased him.

Eli nodded. "I'll look around. I'll be back here."

He saw a lot of things he could buy, if he had the money to spare. The stores were well stocked. A well-stocked store spoke of the prosperity of the community. He received a lot of curious stares and kept his face impassive. A couple of men tried to open a conversation, and he avoided the openings. One of the men looked rough. Lane had said the border toughs were all up and down the Kansas-Missouri border.

He walked down a side street and heard swearing.

"Now what the hell am I going to do with you?"

For an instant Eli thought the question was directed at him, and he threw a startled glance toward the speaker.

The man was looking over the fence into a small corral. He had shoulders like a bull and arms to match. Eli didn't need the leather apron and the blacksmith shop to the left of the corral to tell him this man's occupation. Those brawny arms were the trade-mark of all blacksmiths.

He thought the man was having trouble with the horse in the corral, and asked, "Can I help you?"

The horse didn't look as though it could cause anyone trouble. It stood with drooping head, a heavy-footed draft animal. But still, it could be sensitive about its hoofs being handled.

The blacksmith put a sour look on Eli. "I don't know how. Unless you want to buy this critter. Goddam Bill Jones," he said explosively. "I didn't want to give him credit when I shod this animal. But he talked me into it. He promised to pay me in a week. I know Bill Jones's promises. I kept his horse. I wish now I hadn't."

"Why?"

"Because I got to feed him," the smith said gloomily. "Bill Jones got himself drowned. I just heard about it yesterday."

Eli moved to the fence and inspected the animal. It had age on it and would probably weary before the day was out. It wasn't in the best of flesh, and its coat was scuffy and dirty, but the horse still had years of work left in it. It could pull a plow, if a man was patient with its slow plodding. A man could ride it, and again his patience would be called into play. Anything much above a walk would be beyond this animal.

Eli asked, "How much do you want for him?"

The blacksmith really looked at him for the first time. His eyes narrowed, and he said, "How much will you give for him?"

"I'm not pricing your stock for you."

The blacksmith grinned. The young man had sold some stock of his own, or at least had been around when stock was sold.

He said, "Twenty-five dollars takes him."

"Throw in a saddle?"

The blacksmith shook his head. "I haven't got one."

Eli grinned. "There's no harm trying. I'll take him."

The blacksmith said "Sold," and thrust out his hand. He had a powerful grip. Eli had to work to keep his face from showing it.

The blacksmith had a surge of generosity. "I'll throw in a couple of old blankets and a bridle."

The bridle was good. Eli folded the blankets and placed them on the animal's back. He was used to riding bareback, but this would be better.

The horse responded docilely to the reins, and Eli rode him out of the corral. He stopped and looked at the smith. "What's his name?"

"I never heard Bill Jones call him one." The blacksmith grinned at the picture of the young man astride the tired, old draft animal. "Why don't you call him Dandy?"

Eli said, "It's a good name. Come on, Dandy."

He rode the animal back to the restaurant. The big hoofs plop-plopped against the street. Dandy didn't make much speed, but he could raise a lot of dust.

He tied the horse to the hitch-rack and waited for Lane. Dandy looked even worse standing beside Lane's mare. Eli rested a hand on Dandy's withers. He wasn't unhappy with him at all. Dandy belonged to him.

Ten minutes passed before Lane came into view. He led a chestnut horse, keeping pressure on the lead reins, and it danced behind him. This animal had spirit.

Eli moved out into the street, and Lane stopped. Lane's eyes were glowing. "What do you think of him?"

The chestnut was almost a match for the mare, and Eli's eyes held a wistful look. "He's a lot of horse."

Lane tried to hand the reins to Eli. "You can buy him for a hundred and twenty-five dollars. Plus another twenty-five for the saddle and bridle."

Eli shook his head. "I don't want him." That was a lie.

Lane stared at him, a slight red tinge staining his face. "I talked my head off to get him for this price. You don't think you can walk all over Kansas, do you?"

"I don't plan to."

Lane's breathing sounded louder, and a baffled look was in his eyes. "You can afford him, can't you?"

"I can afford him." That was another lie. Eli could have afforded the chestnut before he bought Dandy. But he couldn't have afforded the saddle, too.

"Damn it," Lane exploded. "After I go to all this trouble—"

Eli hadn't asked him to go to any trouble. He thought he'd better stop Lane before he said something both of them would regret. "I bought a horse."

Some of the anger cleared from Lane's face. "That's more like it. Why didn't you say so. Where is this horse?"

"Standing beside your mare."

Only Dandy was beside the mare, and Lane stared incredulously. The anger came back to his face, and his voice sounded choked. "Is this some kind of a joke?"

"No joke. I own him."

"Good God. Do you plan to ride into Kansas on that thing? You'll look like a ragtag."

Anger mirrored in Eli's face. "I'm the one who's got to worry about how I look. You don't have to ride with me. I hope you can take the chestnut back."

He untied Dandy's reins and jumped up onto his back. He never looked at Lane as he passed him. He plodded down the street, feeling quite a sense of loss. He had liked Jim Lane. Lane must have been used to authority. It showed in his manner and in his words. But he would have to learn he couldn't make every decision for a man. There were a lot of things a man just had to decide for himself.

He wasn't going to have any trouble finding Kansas. The road leading into it was pounded hard and flat by the passage of many wheels and hoofs. All a man had to do was to follow it.

CHAPTER FIVE

Lane caught up with Eli two miles out of Westport. Eli expected to see him go on by, but Lane pulled the mare down to Dandy's slow pace. Eli was aware of Lane's study, but he didn't look his way. He felt no need to apologize to him.

Lane said, "I took the chestnut back."

"I hope you didn't lose any money on him."

"No." It had cost Lane twenty dollars to persuade the chestnut's former owner to take the animal back, but he was wise enough not to tell Eli that. The plop of the horses' hoofs was the only sound for a quarter of a mile, then Lane asked, "Eli, you wanted to own that horse. I saw the way you looked at him."

"Yes," Eli said, "I wanted to own him."

"You said you could afford him."

Eli glanced at him. "I could have afforded him before I bought Dandy. I couldn't have afforded the saddle and bridle."

"Good Lord." The exasperation was back in Lane's voice. "I could've loaned you what you needed."

Eli's eyes were cold. "I don't buy what I can't afford. I don't borrow money to buy what I can't afford." He hadn't intended making that much explanation to Lane.

Lane said helplessly, "Oh Lord. I am a bumbling fool. Eli, will you forgive me? I was only trying to be of help." The native charm was back in his voice.

Eli said, "I'm glad you caught me. I've already told you how much I owe you. But there are some things I've got to decide for myself."

Lane's smile broadened. "I won't make the stupid mistake of trying to do your thinking again, Eli. I promise." He leaned over and thrust out his hand.

Eli sighed as he took it. "I felt kind of lost out here by myself," he admitted. His liking for Lane increased. It looked as though Lane could bump up against a difference of opinion and not feel anger or hurt. To Eli, it was the mark of a big man.

"It's a vast and lonely land," Lane said. "Given to the Indians by treaty for as long as the grass grows and the water flows."

"Did we take it away from them?"

Lane's face was grave. "Steal might be a better word for it.

All this land was promised to the Delaware, the Shawnee, the Kickapoos and the Iowas. It's good land, and the white man, across the Missouri River, couldn't stand to see it in Indian hands. You'd be surprised at the pressure voters can build up on Congress. So we negotiated a new treaty with the Indians, moving them farther west. A few dollars, a few wagonloads of trade goods, and the Indian signed a new treaty. A treaty with the promise that the new land will be his as long as the grass grows and the water flows."

"Will he believe that treaty any more than the one that was broken?"

"I doubt it. But I think he knows he can't stop the tide rolling over him. Until he's settled on land that nobody wants, treaties will be made and broken."

"It sounds kind of rotten."

"It's called progress, Eli. You can't stop it. I told you no man moves without a selfish motivation. Didn't you come out here with one?"

Eli gave him a reluctant nod. "I guess I did."

"And if you refuse to take up a claim, will it give the Indian back his lands?"

"No," Eli said slowly.

"So you accept the way things are and forget it."

Lane saw the troubled expression on Eli's face and said dryly, "It's a little late for you to be worrying about the Indian. Have you noticed that most of this land we've been riding through is already claimed? A man has to ride thirty or forty miles into Kansas to find open land. I'll bet every claim we see was made by a Missourian. It's only a short jump over the border for them, and most of them didn't wait for the official opening."

He pointed to a blazed tree. "There's another one. If we were close enough, you could read the date and the name of the man who claimed it."

"I've seen stakes driven in the ground with a piece of paper or cardboard on them."

Lane nodded. "That's legal, too. Within ten days the claimant is supposed to put up the foundation of his house. Then he must build a house not less than twelve feet square. The foundation can be six-inch logs, not less than twelve feet in length."

"I don't see any building." Eli turned to look at the lonely foundation.

"In a great many cases, you won't. Many of these claims were grabbed for speculative purposes. The owners will sell out to the best bidder."

"That can't be legal," Eli said indignantly.

Lane's smile was bleak. "Who's going to check, and who's going to put them off? There's not much law here, yet. A stronger man can throw a weaker man off and reclaim that man's land."

"How does the weak man protect himself?"

"The few scattered communities have banded together into clubs. They make the local laws by majority vote. You file your claim with the nearest club, and they give you what protection they can. Sometimes it isn't enough."

Eli's face was thoughtful. A man's ability to hold the land he claimed might depend solely on his arms and his determination. It was a sobering thought but not a dismaying one.

He said, "I wanted to claim four quarters. Can I claim that much?"

Lane's eyes were appraising. "A square mile. That's ambitious."

"I don't plan on it all being mine. I'm thinking of my father and brothers."

"You can have that much if you can afford it."

Eli didn't miss the sly thrust. The purchase of Dandy wasn't entirely forgotten.

Lane said, "All you have to do is to shake together a cabin, break half an acre of sod and fence it. Then file your notice of intention to pre-empt your four quarters at the nearest sutler's office. The price will be a dollar and twenty-five cents an acre."

At the price Lane quoted, six hundred and forty acres

amounted to eight hundred dollars. It was a huge sum, a sum far beyond Eli's reach.

Lane laughed at the stricken look on Eli's face. "That sum doesn't have to be put up right away. The land can't be sold until government surveys are completed. Some people say it will take months. They are overly optimistic. I know the way government moves. It will take years. You'll have the use of the land for all that time. When the survey is finally completed, eight hundred dollars will buy that square mile. It will be assigned to you and your heirs forever."

Eli had a faraway look in his eyes, and Lane asked half mockingly, "You are planning on heirs, aren't you?"

"I'm planning on them," Eli said simply. He thought of Alicia. Ah God, how he was planning on them.

Lane saw that Eli intended saying no more on the subject. He had with him one of those men who were reticent when it came to intimate details. It was difficult for a man to learn anything about them, and it was difficult to fasten a hold on them.

He said curtly, "I'd like to reach Wakarusa by nightfall. Can't you kick that animal into a faster gait?"

Eli didn't catch the curtness. He grinned and said, "I'll try. But I'll bet he has only two gaits. The other one will be slower than this."

Lane forced a smile at Eli's small joke. He would be dealing with many such yokels. He must remember to curb his impatience with them.

Eli asked, "Where is this Wakarusa?" He drubbed at Dandy's flanks with his heels. Dandy responded with a small increase in speed.

"It's the only settlement for miles. It's named after a nearby creek. The name isn't official yet. Some people call it New Boston. The Missourians call it Yankee town. You'll find the land you want somewhere near the settlement."

Eli drubbed Dandy's flanks again. If they reached Wakarusa tonight, he could begin his search in the morning.

It was after dark when they reached the settlement. If it hadn't been for the lights in the few, scattered homes, a man could have passed it in the dark, never realizing a settlement was near. Eli saw the orange glow of lamps shining through tent walls. At a quarter-mile angle from the last tent was a grass-thatched mud hut. The family who owned the shake cabin of cottonwood next to the mud hut must have been the first one here, progressing from tent to this more durable structure. The most imposing building in the settlement was a two-storied affair. The sun had worked hard on its cottonwood siding, curling and cracking it.

Lane pulled up before the building and dismounted. He had been in a grumpy mood for the last few miles, barely answering when Eli spoke to him.

Eli felt no resentment. Lane was an older man. He would feel the long ride more than Eli did, and Eli felt it. In the last five miles Dandy's backbone had grown sharper with every step, and the folded thickness of the blankets wasn't enough to offset the sharpness.

Dandy was tired, too. He stood with drooping head, blowing soft snorts of protest.

A man appeared at Eli's elbow, materializing so suddenly out of the darkness that it startled him. The man said, "Jim, is that you?"

Lane grunted a reply.

"I expected you several hours ago. Did you run into trouble?"

"No trouble."

Eli wasn't sure whether or not the words held sarcasm.

Lane said, "Sam, I want you to meet Eli Dryden. Eli, this is Sam Walker."

Walker was a big man. He stood almost as tall as Eli and had a massiveness that far exceeded the younger man's. Yet there was no impression of fat about him. He had a good handshake, sure and forceful. "Glad to meet you, Dryden."

Eli returned the handclasp. "The same," he said. He liked

the big man's voice. There was quiet assurance in it. He couldn't see Walker's face plainly.

He said, "Mr. Walker, I'd like to feed and water my horse."

Walker chuckled. "You'll find no grain here, if that's what you're looking for. But there's plenty of grass near the water trough a block down the street."

Lane said, "Take the mare with you, Eli. After you water her, strip off the saddle and picket her. You'll find pins in the saddlebags."

The darkness hid Eli's frown. That sounded too much like an order. He let the small anger slip away. He owed Lane several favors.

Lane said, "Sam, can we get something to eat at Ma Grundy's?"

Walker pointed at the light coming from a tent down the street. "She's still open. It won't be much."

"It never is," Lane growled. He started down the street, then said over his shoulder, "Eli, join us there. Bring the saddle blankets. We'll need something to sleep on."

The frown was back on Eli's face. Lane's manner had changed the moment he set foot in Wakarusa. It had become crisp and authoritative.

He led the horses to the watering trough. He stood sagging with weariness as they drank. The night was moonless, and the few stars had little power against the darkness. It was an unfriendly sky, he thought somberly. There had been dark nights in Ohio, but this one was different. Back there he knew what the morning would bring. Here, it was obscure as the night itself. That wave of loneliness washed over him again.

He stripped the saddle from the mare and left it on the ground. He picketed Dandy and the mare and listened to them chopping at the grass. It sounded as though they were in lush grass. He turned and trudged toward Ma Grundy's tent.

Lane and Walker were seated at a crude table when Eli brushed aside the tent flap. Walker glanced at him and smiled.

The smile spread from his lips to his eyes. Eli returned it instinctively.

"Sit down," Walker said, and he pushed back a rickety chair. "I was afraid that chair wouldn't hold me."

Eli lowered himself gingerly into the chair. Its joints creaked under his weight. He shrugged and said, "I've picked myself up before."

Those brown eyes gave him swift appraisal. "I imagine you have," Walker said. He looked slow and ponderous, but there was a quickness in his eyes that belied that first impression. He had huge hands, and the fingers were blunt and thick. Those hands were no strangers to hard work. "You'd better order bacon and corn bread," he said. Amusement lighted his eyes. "You have no other choice."

A woman waddled toward the table, carrying two tin plates. She was fat and old, and her dress wasn't too clean, but she had a cheerful face. She set the plates down before Lane and Walker. "I'll bring your coffee in a minute. I'm warming it."

"How old is it, Ma?" Walker asked.

She made a face at him. "Only yesterday's, Sam. You didn't think I was going to throw out all those good grounds, did you?"

Walker laughed. "We're in luck tonight. Usually the grounds are at least a week old. Bring my friend here a plate."

She filched Walker's plate from before him. She gave it to Eli and said severely, "For being so smart, Mr. Sam Walker, you'll wait for yours." She turned and waddled toward the rear of the tent.

Eli tried to hand the plate back, and Walker grinned. "Keep it. Ma and I have a running feud. She'd be disappointed if she couldn't keep ahead of me."

Lane was scowling at the banter. He asked impatiently, "How are things going, Sam?"

"People are coming in by boatfuls and wagonloads. Robinson has promised that the aid society is sending us a steam sawmill right away. We could have us a fair-sized town here by fall."

Ma Grundy came back with another plate of food. She said, "It'll be the first promise Charley Robinson ever kept. He doesn't know what to do with all these people coming in. He's running around like a chicken with its head cut off. I'm glad you're back, Mr. Lane. We need somebody around here, somebody who knows what he's doing."

"Haven't I been here?" Walker yelped.

Walker's levity displeased Lane. Ma Grundy saw the look he gave Walker and held her tongue.

Eli could feel some kind of a bitter argument trembling in the background. He didn't want it exploding on the scene. He wanted no part of it touching and maybe drawing him into it in some way.

He said, "Mrs. Grundy, I've never eaten better corn bread." It was good corn bread, as light and fluffy as any he had ever eaten. The bacon was crisp, and the coffee, while strong, was good. He had no doubt that Ma Grundy was a good cook.

She smiled her pleasure. "You can call me Ma, son."

Walker said soberly, "To give Robinson his due, people are coming in too fast for him to handle. He simply hasn't the accommodations."

Lane snapped, "Then he shouldn't have been selected as the society's agent. He's paid to solve the problems out here."

Walker didn't shake his head, but Eli had the feeling the gesture was there.

"He's a damned timber thief," Lane said. The name Robinson seemed to have enraged him. He looked at Eli. "He's been going around with armed men cutting trees on claims of absent owners. No wonder he wants a sawmill here. Any lumber he saws will be almost clear profit."

"That charge has never been proved against him, Jim," Walker protested.

Lane looked at him with burning eyes. "You don't believe it, Sam?"

The good humor was slipping from Walker's face. "I only said, it's never been proved. I told you people are coming in since you've been gone. They are. Both sides. The border ruffians are pouring in as fast as our people. Big men, tough men. A lot of them spoiling for a fight. You know how they feel about us claiming land they think should belong to them. I'm only trying to tell you that if we split up and fight among ourselves, it'll make it a lot easier for them."

Lane shut his eyes and shook his head. When he reopened them, the anger was gone. "Was there ever a time when you weren't right, Sam? I'm not thinking clearly any more."

"You're worn out," Walker said gruffly. "Don't you think I know how important it was for you to carry news of our position to the outside world?"

Lane shook his head ruefully. "Some success, Sam. More failure. Some of the people in Washington will listen. Others won't." His face darkened. "By God, they will listen. They'll have to."

Walker stood and asked, "Is everybody finished? I think it's time all of us got some sleep." There was affection in his eyes as he looked at Lane. He made a fist and hit Lane's shoulder. "Come on, Jim. Let's turn in."

Lane gave him a weary smile. "You're right again, Sam." Fatigue pulled at his facial muscles. He turned and went out of the tent.

Walker paid Ma Grundy. Eli tried to, the least he could do was to pay his share, but Walker wouldn't hear of it. He threw his arm companionably across Eli's shoulders. "You can even it up later."

Eli asked, "You've known Jim Lane a long time?"

"Not too long." Walker's face was thoughtful. "And yet it seems as if I've known him all my life. He's that kind of a man. He reaches out and takes hold of you quick. We did some exploring here, before the territory was opened. Jim is positive that Kansas will make a great state."

Lane's irritable voice sounded from outside the tent. "Are you two coming?"

"It will be a great state if we don't tear it apart," Walker went on. "It's going to take leadership to prevent that. And

I think Jim Lane is that leader. He's going to need a lot of help, though. And some people buck him."

Eli caught the feeling in Walker's voice. Through Walker's eyes he had a new perspective of Lane. He said, "He did a lot for me. He saved my life."

He recounted the scene in Kansas City, and Walker whistled.

"You knocked out Tim Copple? Hey, I'm going to have to remember to walk lightly around you."

Eli grinned, then his face sobered. "Jim stopped five of them from rushing me. They were all armed. They could've taken him, but something in his face stopped them."

Walker nodded. "I've seen the same thing before."

Lane thrust his head through the flaps, and his face was furious. "Goddam it, Sam. Do I have to stand out here all night?"

Walker said, "Eli was just telling me how you turned tail and ran before those bordermen in Kansas City." He knew how to handle Lane, for Lane's face cleared.

Lane chuckled. "They scared me to death. Eli was the one who stood up to them. Sam, you missed a pleasant sight, seeing Copple stretched out on the floor."

Walker said, "I can imagine."

"Now can we get some sleep? Eli, will you bring those blankets?"

Eli picked up the blankets. There was still an order in Lane's request, but this time he didn't mind it. During the telling of that scene to Walker, he had relived it. He had re-tasted the fear and the anxiety. Gratitude should be stretched, stretched to cover differences of opinion and minor irritations.

Walker said, "Come on, Eli. Your downy bed of feathers is waiting for you."

CHAPTER SIX

Sam Walker was the first to awaken in the morning. The first floor of the two-storied building was crowded with sleeping figures. A man had to be careful where he walked, or he trod upon somebody. The second floor was just as crowded. He had heard many comments of outrage and indignation when these people had learned their sole accommodations were the two bare floors of this building. This was real hardship to them, and Walker grunted. Hell! Sleeping outdoors in this kind of weather wouldn't have been a hardship.

Most of these people came from the Northeast, and they expected to find accommodations equal to those in cities founded fifty years ago. Many of these people were well educated, and as far as refinement went, they were a far cry from the men living along the western border of Missouri. Most of the bordermen were little more than a step removed from actual illiteracy. Everything about the two factions was diametrically opposed. The Eastern man's speech was precise and grammatical, and Walker had heard the frontiersmen jeer at it. Doubtless it sounded affected to Western ears. The Westerner broadened his vowels, and if he knew a basic rule of grammar, his speech didn't show it. The Easterner had known a better way of life, and the big question was, could he adapt to this rough frontier? The bordermen could. Give them a jug of whisky and they could take the most miserable hardships.

Walker grinned bleakly. Perhaps the Eastern immigrants should cease being so temperate. A few hard jolts of whisky put a different complexion on most things.

The two factions had one impulse in common—the desire for land. That tiny bit of common ground wasn't enough for all of them to stand upon. There were too many traits that warred with each other. There was enough land in Kansas for all, but that wasn't going to be the dominant consideration. One side or the other had to impose its will. Walker sighed and shook his head. Man was a quarrelsome animal.

He wanted land as badly as the rest of them. But more, he wanted peace in which to work that land. The first was an accomplished factor—his claim was staked out. At the moment the second seemed as remote as the moon.

He stared soberly at the sleeping Lane. The morning light was harsh against Lane's face, and the beard stubble high-lighted the prominent cheekbones. He thought there were depths to Jim Lane no one would ever probe. Lane was a man restless and demanding of spirit, a man driven by some secret goal. It wasn't land. Lane had staked out a claim near Walker's, but after its doing, he showed little more interest. Walker didn't care what the goal was. This country needed Jim Lane. He had a charm of personality and a persuasive tongue. He could take all these disorganized people flowing into Kansas and weave them into a common tapestry. And Walker was convinced that only by a united front would these people be able to stay here. Charley Robinson couldn't weave that tapestry. He couldn't see much farther ahead than tomorrow, and he was too engrossed in his own interests to help the common cause.

Lane was filled with impatience, and that impatience often spilled over into anger. Walker bore that anger patiently. He thought the anger sprang from the fact there was so much to do and so little time to do it in. Yes, Kansas needed Jim Lane.

Walker's eyes went from Lane to Eli. The sunlight streamed through the glassless window, revealing no shadows, no hag-gard lines in that calm, young face. Eli looked so young, but he wasn't defenseless. No man was who stood up to people like Tim Copple. The magic of Jim Lane had touched Eli in one chance meeting and bound the young man to him. Walker shook his head. It was a rare quality.

He reached down and shook Lane awake. "Are you going to sleep the morning away?"

Lane glared at him, then his face cleared. He sat up and winced. "Lord, Sam. The years make the hours of sleep short and the bed hard." He looked at Eli. "I'd give a lot for his age."

"Who wouldn't?" Walker grunted. "He's sold on you, Jim."

The brusqueness of Lane's nod bothered Walker. Lane accepted the statement too matter-of-factly.

"Sam, I wish you could have seen him standing up to Copple. He knew there were enough of them to stomp him to death, and he never broke. That's raw courage. I wish I had a hundred like him." Lane stood and hunched his shoulders, then straightened them. He looked with distaste at his wrinkled clothing. "Sometimes I wonder if I'll ever sleep in a bed again."

"We've got to build roofs first to put them under," Walker said.

Lane frowned at the sleeping people. Their clamor would besiege him all day. They would pound at him, asking for help, asking for guidance.

"I've got to see Robinson right away," Lane said, "and see if we can get this mess straightened out."

"Go easy on him, Jim. He's a proud man. He sees a threat in you to his standing."

Lane's laugh was harsh. "I don't want his damned job."

"It's more than that, Jim. You know what I mean."

The impatience was back in Lane's face. "I haven't time to worry about his feelings." He stepped over a sleeping man, then stopped. "I promised Eli I'd show him around today. Look after him, Sam, will you?"

Walker said cheerfully, "I'll get him settled. You'd better take time to eat breakfast." He watched Lane move away and doubted he had heard.

He prodded Eli with his boot toe. Eli came instantly awake.

"Another lazy one," Walker said.

Eli grinned at him. He didn't stretch or wince before he got to his feet. He looked toward the spot vacated by Lane, and a small disappointment touched his face.

Walker interpreted the look correctly. "Jim asked me to take you over. He said you were interested in the land around here. I know of a couple of pieces I want to show you."

He thought there wasn't much enthusiasm in Eli's nod. If Jim Lane had proposed looking at the same ground, the enthusiasm would have been there. That was the kind of magic Lane had.

He said, "Everybody turns to Jim for their needs. I swear I believe he even wipes noses." He said it without rancor or jealousy, and Eli grinned.

"I'm big enough to wipe my own." People were beginning to stir all over the building, and Eli said, "Let's get out of here before the rush starts."

"And before they eat up everything," Walker said. "You hungry?"

"I can always eat."

Walker suspected as much. Youth burned up a lot of food, and it rarely had the burden of a sour stomach. "We can wash at the horse trough. What do you want for breakfast?"

"Do I have a choice?"

Walker said sadly, "You do, if it's bacon and corn bread. Sometimes, I order corn bread and bacon for a change."

Eli laughed. Walker was an easy man to be around.

They walked to the trough and splashed water into their faces. Eli dried his hands on his shirttail.

Walker said dryly, "I've had people ask me where the towels were."

Eli grinned and walked toward Dandy. He took him off the picket pin and led him to the trough. Walker studied the horse with a thoughtful eye, and Eli waited defiantly for his comment.

Walker said, "He won't go fast, but I'd say he'll go far enough. He'll be useful when you get your land."

The defiance slipped away. Walker understood a man's problems.

Eli let Dandy drink his fill. Not all of that swollen belly

was water. The grass had been good last night. He repicketed him, then watered Lane's mare.

Walker said, "You take care of your animals." It could have been a casual observation, or a pointed reference to the fact that Lane had made no attempt to see to the mare's needs this morning.

Lane's saddle was still on the ground, and Eli asked, "What shall I do with it?"

"Leave it. We have no thieves here."

It jarred against Eli's sense of order, but if Walker and Lane weren't concerned about it, he shouldn't be.

Walker was right about breakfast. It was bacon and corn bread.

Eli said, "I'd give a lot for a couple of fresh eggs."

Walker scowled at him in mock anger. "You are a disturbing influence. I've forgotten what an egg tastes like.

"Ma does the best she can," he said as they left the tent. "I'll get my horse and be right with you."

He had a good, solid animal, a buckskin with a black mane and tail. The horse wasn't cut for speed, but everything about him said endurance.

"I like him," Eli said.

Walker's face brightened at the praise. "I bought him in Illinois and have never regretted it. Lane's mare can run circles around him for a while, but he'll still be going at day's end. I'll take endurance over flash any day."

"Unless somebody's chasing me," Eli said.

Walker chuckled. "You got an argument. Any particular direction you want to start?"

Eli shook his head. "I'll just follow you."

As they rode out of town Walker said, "You won't know this place in a few more months. We've got the people. All we need is the building. And that will come. I've been over a lot of Kansas. Right around here isn't a bad place to settle down."

"I imagine most of the good land is already claimed around here."

Walker threw him a keen glance, then said, "Yes, it is. You have to go pretty far out from town. But I can't see that a few more miles matters."

Eli was sweeping the country with his eyes, and Walker felt just a tinge of irritation. He threw out a pointed observation, but Eli didn't bother to pick it up.

"What kind of soil is it?" Eli asked.

"Good rich vegetable mold, from a foot and a half to seven feet deep, underlaid by clay and limestone. It will grow all kinds of produce, including hemp. I wintered here last year. It wasn't too bad at all. Cattle do well, and hogs can live on the nuts in the forest. Once a man gets the prairie sod broken—" He shut up abruptly. Eli's eyes were sweeping the country again. Walker wondered if Eli even heard him.

Eli heard him, all right. He absorbed every bit of information he could get about this land. He liked what he saw, but still it wasn't quite right. He didn't know how he could tell, but he would know when he saw the exact spot he wanted. Maybe he was being too particular. A man couldn't go too far wrong with any of this. The country was rolling and apparently free from marshes and swamps. Good stands of timber grew along the creek bottoms, and he recognized black walnut, hickory, lin and hackberry trees. The cottonwoods made a pleasant rustling sound in the breeze. Whoever had cut lumber for that two-storied building in Wakarusa didn't know their timber very well. Cottonwood was durable, but unless it was cured for a long time, it twisted and warped.

Walker was tired before the end of the day. "How many hills do you have to see over?" he grumbled. "It's time we turned back. As it is it'll be dark before we get to Wakarusa."

Eli nodded agreeably.

Both men were silent on the return trip. Eli was thinking of the country he had seen all day. Walker was thinking of Eli. Eli was pleasant company to be with, but he didn't communicate very well. One never knew exactly what he was thinking. One thing was for certain. Eli Dryden had an independent mind. No one was going to capture it easily.

Eli watered Dandy and picketed him. Walker was right about the time of arrival. It was after dark.

Walker said, "I thought you'd stake out a claim."

Eli shook his head. "I'm going to look a little more. I thought I'd ride south tomorrow."

"Then for God's sake get a saddle," Walker said explosively. "Before you cut yourself in two." His legs felt stiff and cramped. He knew if he had ridden bareback all day he would spend the next week standing. "See old man Chastain. He's got some secondhand saddles." He pointed to a grass-thatched mud hut. "He won't hold you up."

"I'll see him," Eli said. He started to move, and Walker said, "Get yourself a gun, Eli. If you're going around by yourself, you'll need some protection."

"From Indians?"

Walker shook his head. "That danger is rare. From the border toughs. We had two fist fights last week. Before it's all over, guns will be used."

Stubbornness crept into Eli's face. "You sound like Lane. Is everybody around here determined there has to be a war?"

Walker controlled his irritation. Youth knew everything. He kept his voice level. "A man needs a gun if for no other reason than to live off the country."

He turned abruptly. He didn't intend for his departure to be civil.

He found Lane just coming out of Ma Grundy's tent. Lane looked like a man with a million things on his mind.

He said absently, "Hello, Sam." He added, almost as an afterthought, "Did Dryden find his land?"

"We rode until my tail ached. Nothing suited him. He's riding south in the morning."

"After all I've done for him," Lane exploded. "He can't do that. I want him here."

He took a stride, and Walker seized his arm. "Don't try to talk to him in the mood you're in, Jim. It'll end up in an argument." He shook his head. "He's a hard-headed one, but he's got a right to go where he pleases." His face turned thoughtful. "We're going to need good men all over Kansas. Maybe it'd be best to let him go and keep in touch with him. He's going anyway," he finished quietly.

Lane struggled with himself, then said abruptly, "Maybe you're right. I've got too much to do to worry about one man."

They didn't find Eli that night. They stopped at Chastain's, and the old man said, "He was here a half hour ago. Bought a saddle and rifle."

"Did you sell him junk?" Walker demanded.

"I sold him what he could afford," Chastain said indignantly. "That saddle's got a lot of use in it, and that was a good Jake Hawkins rifle." His indignation mounted. "Did you expect me to sell him my Sharps?"

"No," Walker answered. But the Hawkins rifle was an antiquated weapon compared to the Sharps. He wished Eli had one of the newer rifles.

Lane and Walker spent another hour looking for Eli, and Lane said angrily, "To hell with it."

"I expect he's sleeping out somewhere," Walker said. He didn't blame Eli. That overcrowded building with its assorted smells could hold no attraction for anybody. "Maybe we can catch him in the morning before he leaves. If I know him, he'll be watering his horse before he goes." He doubted Eli had left Wakarusa. A strange country was no place for anybody to be wandering around in after dark.

He lay awake a long time thinking about Eli Dryden. He hated to see him go. A man met a lot of people during his lifetime. Every now and then, a personality reached out and seized you. Dryden had such a personality. Walker could appreciate the qualities in Dryden, even while they irritated him. Maybe he recognized that stubbornness because some of it was in him.

He awakened early in the morning and shook Lane to consciousness. If he judged Eli Dryden right, he would waste little of the daylight. He said, "He'll be leaving."

Lane said grumpily, "Let him go." He rolled over, and

Walker stared at his back. He shook his head and walked out of the building.

He found Eli at the watering trough. Dandy was already saddled, and the ancient saddlebags were bulging. The Hawkins rifle was secured to the horn with a piece of rope. Eli and his horse made a ragtag outfit, but Walker felt no pity or apprehension for him. Eli Dryden might not find the easy way, but he would make it.

Eli's face was blank as he watched Walker approach.

Walker thrust out his hand and said, "I'm glad I caught you before you left."

A smile put animation into Eli's face. "I thought you might be mad because I didn't listen to you."

Walker's astonishment was real. "Why should I be mad? You didn't see the piece of land you wanted. You keep your own ideas, boy. Don't let anybody water them down for you."

Eli nodded. A shadow of trouble was in his eyes as he asked, "Does Jim feel the same way?"

"You mean you think he could be sore because he's not here?" Walker shook his head. "You don't know Jim Lane very well. He didn't get to bed until almost daybreak. The last thing he told me was, 'Sam, if I don't wake up in time to see Eli off, tell him I wish him luck.'"

The shadow left Eli's eyes. "I appreciate what both of you did for me."

"We didn't do anything," Walker said brusquely. "Let us know where you settle."

Eli swung into the saddle. He hesitated a long moment, looking at Walker. Walker and Lane were the only friends he had in this big, empty land. He wished he could have found the claim he wanted near here.

He said, "I will," and kicked Dandy into a slow trot.

"How about provisions?" Walker called after him.

Eli patted the bulging saddlebags. He had a typical Kansas menu in them—bacon and corn meal. He could bake his corn bread and fry his bacon in the battered skillet in the right-hand saddlebag.

He looked back after fifty yards. Walker hadn't moved. Eli raised his hand in a salute, and Walker returned it.

Eli rode for four days but not in a steady direction. He followed watersheds and creek bottoms, veering as they veered. He had squirrel twice and prairie chicken once for his evening meal. The old rifle held true. He didn't see a soul during that time. He could imagine he was alone in an empty world. Yet, he knew a peace. He lay back and watched the dying coals of the evening's campfire and thought of Alicia. And he wasn't alone at all.

He judged that as a crow flies he was between forty and fifty miles southeast of Wakarusa. He felt a tingle of excitement begin in his veins. He liked this country. It was flatter than the land around Wakarusa, and still it wasn't bottom land. It would retain moisture longer than upland ground, and yet there was enough slope to it that water wouldn't stand on it during a heavy rainy season and drown crops. Up on the horizon was a thick bank of timber, denoting a large creek or a river. He saw a grove of wild pecan trees, and his guess about this soil retaining moisture was confirmed, for pecan trees liked for their feet to be wet. Hogs would thrive in that grove, and the squirrels would be large and plump. Somewhere in this vicinity he would find his land.

A half mile ahead of him a thin band of trees snaked across the country, marking the course of a small stream. He would noon there and let Dandy drink and graze.

He heard the sound of a voice a quarter-mile from the stream. He stopped Dandy and listened. At first he thought an argument was going on, then he realized he heard only a lone voice. He couldn't make out the words, but from the sound of it, an extremely angry man was ahead of him. He started Dandy moving again, and the caution of not knowing what was ahead was in his face.

The land sloped gently toward the creek. Now the creek wasn't ten feet wide, though its high banks said that in rainy weather it carried a great deal more water.

A narrow band of rock shelved through the creek bottom, making an excellent low-water bridge. He was right about there being just one man here. And it wasn't hard to see the cause of his rage. He had run his wagon off the shelf of rock, and the left-hand wheels were mired in the mud, canting the wagon precariously. The light team was apparently unable to pull the wagon free and back onto the bridge. The man was trying to push the wagon, flog the team, and swear at the same time. The swearing was the most successful. He had an awesome string of oaths. He was soaked to the knees and mud-besplattered. The team's hoofs flailed the water, fanning a spray back of them, soaking both man and wagon. Each time it happened, he found some new name to call them.

Eli sat and listened. He had seen angry men in his life but never one like this. This one was wild.

He waited until the man stopped to catch his breath, then asked, "Are you in trouble?"

The man jumped at the unexpected voice and whirled. He was short of height, and his shoulders were so massive that they looked out of proportion. He had a bushy shock of black hair crowning the homeliest face Eli had ever seen. The jaw was too big, the nose too long and broad. He had teeth as big as a horse's, crowding a crooked mouth.

The massive chest heaved as the man considered Eli's question. He glared at Eli, then bellowed, "Am I in trouble? Of all the goddamed stupid questions."

CHAPTER SEVEN

"I can ride on and leave you mired down," Eli said.

The big chest heaved. "Ride on. Who needs you?"

Eli lifted the reins.

The man threw out a pleading hand. "No, don't. I been in here three hours already."

The anger was fading from the man's face. Without passion distorting it, the face wasn't nearly as awesome. It was still ugly, but Eli decided it was a comfortable ugliness.

The man grumbled, "Do you want me to get down on my knees and beg?"

"No. Just keep a civil tongue in your head."

A flare of temper appeared in those brown eyes, then faded as quickly as it showed. The man chuckled. "You sound like Lacey." He had a fine smile. It softened the harsh contours of his face and drove the ugliness away. He waded to the bank and thrust a hand at Eli. "Cass Bromley. And I'm grateful you came along. It'll be after dark before I get home. Lacey will be worrying."

Eli felt the strength in the hand. He replied, "Eli Dryden. You got a rope in that wagon?"

Bromley said, "I have." He studied Dandy curiously.

Eli smiled. "He's short on looks."

Bromley laughed. "I was just thinking we'd make a pair."

The man had a wry sense of humor, and Eli decided he could like him. Eli started to swing down, and Bromley said, "I'm wet already. I'll get it." He waded back to the wagon.

He knotted one end of the rope about the wagon tongue. Eli noted with approval that the knots were secure. One could tell a meticulous man by the way he did a simple task. Haste always led to carelessness.

Eli put Dandy into the water, crossing on the natural bridge. He stopped in front of and a little to the right of Bromley's team. He wasn't sure Dandy could pull the wagon back up onto the bridge. If not, he would have to drag it out along side of it.

Bromley threw him the other end of the rope, and Eli knotted it about the horn. He swung down, and the water lapping across the bridge was ankle deep. He had a six-foot length of rope left after the knotting, and he used it as a lash, cutting Dandy across the rump. Dandy looked at him in pained surprise.

Bromley bellowed, "Easy, easy. Do you want to tear the tongue out of my wagon?"

Eli grinned. Dandy wouldn't lunge forward, even under the lashing. He would be lucky to get a slow walk out of Dandy.

He slashed him again, and the horse moved forward. The slack disappeared from the rope, and it stretched humming tight.

Eli urged him into the pull. "Ho, boy. Ho." He held the rope end swinging in his right hand, ready to cut Dandy if he needed it. He had seen horses quit when asked to move a weight like that mired-down wagon.

Bromley's team was slashing the water with their forehoofs. They might carry a wagon along at a spanking rate on the level, but Eli decided they wouldn't be much good where a pull was needed.

Bromley had his shoulders against the tail gate. He wouldn't be doing a lot of good back there. If three horses couldn't pull the wagon out, a man's weight wasn't going to help.

Dandy's head went down, and he dug in those big hoofs. His feet slipped, and he replanted them. He was dogged rather than spectacular. He fought to gain a fraction of an inch, then an inch. His muscles stood out in knotty bunches, and he looked like something carved out of stone.

The wagon wheels were crimped against the edge of the slab rock, and Eli had just about decided Dandy couldn't do it. He expected at any instant to hear a pistol-like report as the rope parted. The front wheels grated against the edge of the rock. The wagon tilted precariously, then came up onto the bridge with a rush. Dandy had to lunge forward to keep ahead of Bromley's team.

Eli heard wild swearing, but his hands were too full to look. He ran beside Dandy, guiding him up the opposite slope of the road. He yelled, "Whoa, boy, whoa," and used Dandy's weight to slow and stop the team. He stopped them as the road leveled out and said in a soothing voice, "Easy now. Easy."

He looked behind him, and Bromley was just standing up.

Water ran from his hair, pushing against the mud on his nose and chin. His hands were covered with it, and gobs of it plastered his shirt front and trousers. Bromley hadn't been braced against the wagon's quick movement, and he had plunged full length into the creek. By the mud on him, he had gone clear to the bottom.

He spat out a mouthful of water and swore. He used his muddy hands trying to clean his face and made it worse.

Eli went into a paroxysm of laughter. Bromley swore at him, and Eli's laughing became harder. The more he tried to control it, the worse it became.

Bromley charged up the slope, and his eyes were furious. "What's so goddamed funny?" he roared.

"You," Eli said and wiped his eyes.

Bromley yelled, "If I thought you done that on purpose—" He took a threatening step toward Eli, then his better sense returned. He looked at his muddy clothes, and a reluctant grin tugged at his mouth. He said a little grimly, "I wish I could reverse it, so I could get me a laugh."

He saw the effort Eli was making trying to keep his face straight. "Go on, laugh, damn you."

"I'm sorry. But if you knew how you looked coming up out of that crick."

"I can imagine." Bromley shook his head. "Lacey will kill me when she sees these clothes. She just took them off the line this morning."

Eli thought Bromley must walk in mortal fear of her. He said, "Wash them in the crick. They'll dry before you're home."

Bromley's face brightened. He sat down and tugged his pants over his boots. The sodden material was stubborn, and he cussed it. He draped shirt and pants over an arm. He wore nothing beneath them. He was powerful through the shoulders and muscle-heavy in the arms. His chest was black with thick, matted hair that covered his belly and extended to his ankles. He stood on short, bandy legs, and his arms were long.

"If you laugh now, I'll take it as a personal affront," Bromley said. But there was a twinkle in his eye. "You tell me how the Lord could make so many mistakes in one man."

Eli's liking for the man increased. It took a good man to poke wry fun at himself.

He said, "I'll wash them for you."

Bromley shook his head. "I'm already soaked."

He waded into the stream and began sloshing his garments in the water. He looked up at Eli and grinned. "I sure hope no woman comes along now. It'd scare her to death."

He hadn't scared Lacey, Eli thought. Maybe she had known Cass Bromley long enough to see the real man encased in that grotesque body.

Bromley finished his washing, waded out of the stream, and spread his shirt and pants in the sunshine. "I hate to put on wet clothes," he said. He stretched out beside Eli on the bank. "I can't even smoke. My tobacco was in my shirt pocket."

Eli pulled a cloth sack out of his pocket and tossed it to him.

Bromley fished his pipe out of his pants pocket. He blew it out and stuffed it full of tobacco. He lit it and puffed out a cloud of smoke. "Ah," he murmured. "You can have my right hand."

Eli laughed. "I'll remember that."

Bromley said mournfully, "Well, I wasted this day. Drove twenty miles for nothing. I heard of a couple of cows for sale. They didn't have a tooth in their heads."

Eli nodded. Bromley was wise not to buy a gummer. When a cow grew old and lost her front teeth, it was difficult for her to graze. Without the necessary amount of grazing she produced little milk.

He said, "I imagine a good cow is at a premium here."

"They are. That's why I went to look at them. Lacey had heard what they really were from somebody. She told me I was a fool to go."

Lacey sounded like a harshly-critical, all-knowing wife. There was nothing more irritating to a man. Eli thought of Alicia, and a pang of loneliness ripped through him.

Bromley asked, "You out here after land?"

Eli nodded. "I didn't see anything around Wakarusa I wanted."

Bromley snorted. "Living around there's like living in a city."

Eli smiled. It took a long stretch of the imagination to call Wakarusa a city.

"The land next to mine hasn't been claimed."

"No?" Eli murmured politely.

"It's just what you're looking for."

Bromley grinned at the rebellion in Eli's eyes. "No man knows what another is looking for. But you can look at it, can't you? Stay the night with us, and I'll show you the land in the morning. Lacey's a hell of a good cook."

Eli's stomach had known rough fare the past several days, and the thought of a home-cooked meal was too tempting to turn down. "That's kind of you," he said.

Bromley felt his clothes. "Dry enough," he grunted. He put them on damp and climbed into the wagon. He picked up the reins and squinted at the sun. "We got about ten miles to go. It'll be after dark, when we get there."

Eli mounted, and Bromley grinned at him. "I'm not the only funny-looking thing around here."

Eli patted Dandy's neck. "He's not much on looks or go. But I'll take him."

"By God, he's stout. I'll bet he can pull a stump out of the ground."

Eli said soberly, "He'll probably get the chance to try it."

Cass Bromley was a comfortable man to be around. Eli would like nothing better than to be neighbors with him. But it depended upon the land.

"Your team can run away from me," Eli warned.

"I'll keep you in sight." Bromley snapped the reins against the team's rumps, and they leaped into full stride. In a quarter mile they were out of view. Dandy plodded patiently after them.

Bromley was waiting for Eli a half mile down the road. He

said, "They're not as full of run as they thought they were."

The team was willing to walk, and Dandy trudged along behind them. Darkness was blending the country into a solid, black mass when Eli saw the orange square of light ahead of him. Nothing was more comforting than a lighted window in the dark. He remembered how he used to come out of the fields after dark at home and how good a light had looked to him. He wondered if a man ever got over homesickness.

The woman must have heard the rattle of wheels as Bromley drove into the yard, for a door opened, and her figure was silhouetted against the light. "Is that you, Cass?" she called.

"It's me. Be right in as soon as I unharness."

Eli couldn't see her face, but her figure was youthfully slender. The timbre of her voice was young, almost girlish. Bromley was at least in his mid-thirties. It looked as though Bromley had married a very young woman. That wasn't so odd. But it was odd that he would let a young woman dominate him.

Bromley hung the harness on a peg driven into a tree. "Haven't got the shed built yet. Just finished the house. I can't offer you oats, but the grass is good."

He drew water from a well and waved aside Eli's offer of help. "Got to get me a pump," he said as he filled a small trough. "Maybe we'd better wash up before we go in."

The darkness hid Eli's grin. Cass Bromley was afraid of Lacey's tongue. The horses, impatient to drink, shouldered at the men as they washed. Eli heard the noisy suck of their drinking as he turned from the trough.

Lacey was waiting for them in the doorway. She said, "Cass Bromley, did you stop at the tavern? Let me smell your breath."

Bromley seized her upper arms, lifted her and set her to one side. "Hush," he said. "We got company."

He turned his head. "Eli, this is Lacey Bromley. Lacey, meet Eli Dryden."

Eli was startled at seeing her. She couldn't have been over seventeen at the most. Her figure was still a girl's figure, but there were hints and suggestions of a future ripening. She was too thin, and her cheekbones stood out prominently. Her mouth was cut on generous lines, but it looked full-lipped and warm. She had magnificent eyes, fringed by a curtain of long, dark lashes. They had an inner light, a luminosity that held a man's attention. Her rich, long hair was black, and the lamplight played in it, dashing it with little touches of red. In a few years she would be a strikingly handsome woman. Perhaps Cass Bromley had seen that, too.

She stared at Eli with a strange intentness, then a faint wave of color stole up from the base of her throat. She nodded stiffly. "I'm pleased to meet you."

Bromley said, "We're starved. How about something to eat?"

She turned on him as though relieved to have an outlet for some oddly pent-up emotion. "Do you expect to walk in here at midnight and have supper waiting for you?" Her eyes widened. "Look at your clothes," she said angrily. "It looks like you've been wallowing in them!"

Bromley threw up his hands. "Was ever a man plagued by such a sister?"

Eli was sure he looked startled this time. Bromley's words explained and changed so many things. He murmured, "Maybe all the plaguing doesn't all come from Miss Bromley."

She gave him a flash of her eyes. "For that, Mr. Dryden, I'll feed you."

Bromley gave him a questioning look. "I'm sheltering a turncoat," he grumbled.

The meal was primitive but excellent. The corn bread was light and fluffy. The catfish were fried to a golden brown, and the flesh beneath the flaky crust was firm and white.

Eli said, "I've never eaten catfish that tasted this good." He was rewarded by the flush of pleasure in Lacey's cheeks.

"Channel catfish," Bromley said. "We catch them in the river near here. I've seen some big devils come out of it." He reached for another piece, then reconsidered. "But a man can get tired of them."

"Not me," Eli disagreed.

"Wait until you eat them for a month straight."

Eli agreed that might pall on a man, but tonight he ate until he could hold no more.

Lacey began clearing the table. "I'm grateful to you for pulling my brother out. I was beginning to worry."

Eli smiled. "If I knew he was so mean, I'd have left him there."

"I wish you'd show me the place," Lacey said. "I might want to push him in again someday."

Bromley said, "A man stands little chance with the two of you plotting against him." His mock frown centered on Eli. "I'm not sure I want you for a neighbor."

Lacey looked at Eli with that odd, luminous intensity in her eyes. "Are you going to be our neighbor?"

Her expression made him feel strange, almost uncomfortable. He said, "I haven't decided yet."

CHAPTER EIGHT

At breakfast Lacey set a platter on the table and said, "That's the last of the bacon."

Bromley sighed. "That means we eat catfish until I can get to town."

"I told you we were running low on several things. I can stretch them just so far."

Bromley grinned at Eli. "Her tongue is worse than a miller's stone. It grinds a man to bits."

Lacey sniffed at him, then turned to minding her corn bread in the big Dutch oven. She looked even better in the daylight. Her skin was clear and fair with the vibrant skin tones of youth.

Bromley was talking to him, and Eli took his eyes from her.

Bromley said, "With the way prices are I hate to go to town. Bacon fifty cents a pound. Corn meal five cents a pound. Keeps a man broke just to eat." His eyes grew indignant. "Do you know what it cost me to have twenty acres of prairie sod broken out? Eighty dollars."

Eli's mouth sagged. That was a lot of money. "I'll buy my own plow before I spend that kind of money."

"You've never broken prairie," Bromley said dryly. "The damned stuff is nothing but a mass of tough roots. It throws a plow around until it jerks a man's arms off. I guess it's worth four dollars an acre to have it done."

Eli said stubbornly, "I'll plow my own land."

Bromley grinned. "Talk to me after you've plowed a few acres. We'll see how much spirit you've got left."

Lacey put a new batch of corn bread on the table.

Bromley shook his head. "Not me."

"I'm full," Eli said. This was the second meal he had eaten here. Should he offer payment? He decided against it. He would have to make repayment in some other way.

Bromley stood and asked, "You ready to go?"

Eli nodded and followed him outside.

Lacey called from the door, "I hope you find what you want."

He waved to her and fell in step with Bromley. He hoped he would, though he was skeptical. But it would be nice to have ready-made neighbors such as these.

"We'll walk," Bromley said.

Eli asked, "If this land is so good, how come somebody else hasn't claimed it?"

"We don't get many people down this far," Bromley answered. "This isn't Wakarusa." A grin worked on his lips. "To tell the truth, I staked out this land. I just didn't write my name on the claim stakes. Unless a man got off and looked close, he'd ride on by, thinking the land was claimed. I guess that kept quite a few away."

Eli grew more skeptical with every stride. Something had

to be wrong with this piece of land Bromley wanted him to see.

He asked bluntly, "Why didn't you want it?"

"Because I like the piece I've got better. I was going to claim it for Sarah, Lacey's married sister. But her man liked something he found around Big Springs better."

They passed a stake driven into the ground. Bromley said, "We're stepping onto it now. I guess I drove in stakes enough to claim over a square mile."

"Why didn't you keep it all?" Eli challenged. A strange excitement was building in him. They walked across prairie, the fine-bladed grass reaching higher than his waist. The sod was thick and spongy. He fingered some of the grass, and Bromley said, "It makes damned fine hay." Then he answered Eli's question. "I thought about keeping it all. I struggled with it for a couple of weeks. Lacey said I couldn't even keep up with what I had. She's right."

The land was gently rolling, sloping toward a thick band of timber.

"That's the river," Bromley pointed out. "A man could cut timber down there the rest of his life and never make a dent. I imagine that old river comes out pretty good in a rainy time. I've seen lots of marks of flooding."

Eli thought, The flooding would never reach this far. The excitement had turned into a drum, and each beat shook his body.

He said, "But why me?"

Bromley grinned. "Because I might get stuck in another crick. You'd be near enough to holler at."

Bromley couldn't have put it any nicer that he wanted Eli to be his neighbor.

He tramped after Eli, and after a couple of hours asked plaintively, "Do you have to look at every square foot of it?"

Eli's eyes caught a copse of trees at the height of a small rise. A meandering line of smaller trees and brush trailed from the copse, running downhill. "Is that a spring up there?"

Bromley nodded. "A good one, too."

Eli lengthened his stride. He reached the crest and looked at the water bubbling up out of the rocky ground. A man could use the scattered rocks to build a basin. He could catch a lot of water before it started its downhill course. He dipped up a double handful and tasted cool, sweet water. His eyes were shining as he looked at Bromley.

He judged he stood on the highest prominence. A man could build here, and every morning his eyes could sweep his land. The spring, so close to the building site, meant easy, available water.

Bromley said, "That's not all the water you'd have. A fair-sized stream cuts through the southwestern corner. I guess you want to see that, too."

"Yes," Eli said, and moved in that direction. Behind him he heard Bromley grumbling, "Walk a man's legs off."

He stood at the creek's edge. In places, it ran deep and broad, then thinned and was shallow, with singing ripples, connecting pool to pool. The exultance in him sang louder than any ripple. He had water and grass and timber. He had acres of unbroken, virgin land. To some people this would be only an expanse of empty land. It wasn't to Eli. He could see pastures dotted with grazing cattle; he could see the fields bursting with thriving crops.

Bromley said, "I get most of my supplies at Trading Post. It's closer than Osawatomie. But if Trading Post hasn't got something a man needs, he can find it in Osawatomie."

He saw no reaction on Eli's face. He didn't know what more a man could want, but then everybody saw things differently. He said dully, "I guess we've seen about most of it."

He turned to retrace his steps home. He thought irritably this Dryden was a close-mouthed one. The least he could do was comment one way or the other.

As they neared a claim stake Eli asked, "How many acres in this piece?"

"You'd have over three hundred acres." Maybe Eli was still interested, and hope revived in Bromley. "Nobody knows for sure what they've got. And they won't until the survey lines are run. The way the government moves that could take years."

Over three hundred acres. Eli was drunk with the words. Why, that was half of the world, at least. And he had the free use of the land until the surveys were run. By the time that happened, if he had any luck at all, he should be able to pay for his land in full. He remembered his goal of a section of land. He couldn't chew it all in one bite—maybe he could make that goal later.

He asked, sober-faced, "Have you got a pencil?"

Bromley was equally sober-faced. "I just happened to bring one. You figuring on writing something?"

"I'm figuring on writing something."

Joy flooded Bromley's face. He thrust out his hand. "Howdy, neighbor."

A delighted grin rode Eli's face. He squeezed Bromley's hand. "Howdy, neighbor."

He took the pencil and wrote his name and date on the claim stake. He traced and retraced the letters and numbers until they stood out bold and black. A man wouldn't have any trouble reading that even from a dozen feet.

Bromley looked as happy as though it had been his own land. "It's almost a square piece. The next claim stake is due south."

Eli made a turn to the south, and Bromley asked, "Where are you going?"

"To write my name on that stake."

"You've walked my legs off already," Bromley protested. "Let's go back and get the horses."

Eli said over his shoulder, "I haven't time to go back for them. I'll see you later."

Bromley shook his head. The crazy fool was going to walk all around the perimeter. On top of all the walking already behind him, it was going to make a long, tiring day. He turned toward his house, and a grin danced on his lips. Did he have news for Lacey! And if he interpreted that glint in her eye correctly, it was going to be mighty interesting news.

CHAPTER NINE

It was after three o'clock before Eli returned to Bromley's house. He stood for a moment and studied it. He wasn't running down Bromley's house, but he wanted a bigger one. With a fireplace, he decided. There was nothing more cheery on a cold winter night than a roaring fire in the fireplace.

Lacey saw him and rushed to the door. She said, "Cass told me, Eli. I'm so glad." She flushed at her use of his first name and murmured, "I'm sorry, Mr. Dryden."

He grinned at her. "Don't be. I'm going to call you Lacey. I figure on being around for a long time."

She gave him a brief, direct look, then lowered her lashes. She seemed overly excited, and he wondered why. He guessed any kind of news was exciting to people who lived a lonely life.

She asked, "Have you had anything to eat?"

"I never thought of it," he answered absently. "I had a drink out of my spring though."

She burst into laughter. "It's yours already?"

He frowned at her. "I signed all the claim stakes. What else is there to do?"

She laid her hand lightly on his arm. "Don't be so touchy. I wasn't poking fun at you. You'll have to ask Cass."

"Is he in the house?"

She nodded. "He says you walked his legs off. I think it's an excuse to get out of working this afternoon."

Bromley was stretched out in a rocker. His eyes were closed.

Eli didn't care if he was asleep. He shook his shoulder. "Cass, what do I do now?"

Bromley opened his eyes and yawned. "What do you do about what?"

"About my land? What do I do to protect it? Those stakes won't be enough, will they?"

"No. You'll have to register it with the squatter's association in Trading Post. Ben Murphy is the registrar. We'll ride in in a few days and see about it."

Eli shook his head. "I haven't got a few days to waste." Enough days were going to pass as it was before he saw Alicia again.

Bromley tugged on his boots. "Are you going to turn out to be one of those people who's always rushing?"

Lacey said tartly, "It wouldn't hurt you to have a little of that quality."

Bromley's face was gloomy. "I should've stayed in that crick."

Lacey walked to the door with them. "I'll hold supper."

Eli said, "Don't. We'll get something to eat in town."

Lacey called after him, "Keep him out of the tavern."

Bromley exploded at the grin on Eli's face. "Don't think you're going to do any watch-doggin' on me."

Eli's face was pious. "I've got to follow orders."

It was ten miles to Trading Post, and Dandy had only one gait—a slow, plodding one. Bromley kept saying, "Kick him up. At this rate it'll be next week before we get back."

"You hear him, Dandy?" Eli asked.

Dandy flicked an ear to dislodge a fly.

"He heard you, Cass. He's thinking about it."

Bromley snorted and resigned himself to Dandy's gait.

It was well after six o'clock when they arrived in Trading Post. Eli saw a blacksmith shop, a general store and a saloon. A few houses clustered around the three business buildings.

Bromley said, "It isn't much of a town, but the smithy can make just about everything you can't buy in the general store. And a man can get whisky and sometimes beer in the saloon. I'll buy a drink." His eyes had a hopeful gleam.

"Not now." Eli wished he could explain to Bromley that he couldn't rest comfortably until he fulfilled every requirement that would make that land his. He saw the gleam fade and said, "We'll stop in after we see the registrar."

"This is the supper hour. You can't bust in on him now."

"Yes I can. Which is his house?"

"The last one on the right. Do you know you're hard-headed?"

Eli grinned as he swung off before Murphy's house. "You'll find other faults," he promised.

A stout, open-faced man answered Bromley's knock. Bromley said, "We won't interrupt your meal more than a minute, Ben. Meet my new neighbor, Eli Dryden. He's claiming that land next to mine."

Murphy eyed Eli sharply and seemed satisfied. "You're getting good land. Wait until I get my notebook and put it down."

He came back with a dog-eared notebook and laboriously scrawled the necessary information. He said, "It's yours. If anybody disputes it, see Judge Conley. He settles all arguments. He's a fair man. You won't have any trouble."

To offset the assurance he added, "But Ross Haines won't like it."

Bromley snorted. "Who cares what that goddamed slaver likes?"

Murphy's eyes were troubled. "He can be nasty, Cass."

"Let him. Thanks, Ben, for your trouble."

"Won't you come in and have a bite?"

Murphy's invitation put a rumble in Eli's belly. "No, sir," he said. "We took up your time at a bad hour as it is."

Murphy shook his hand. "Well, stop in then the next time you're in town."

When they reached the horses, Bromley said indignantly, "What did you turn down that meal for? I'm starving."

"We'll get something at the general store. Who is Ross Haines?"

"He's a Georgia-born pro-slaver. His kind are collected around Atchison and Leavenworth. He ought to feel lonely around here. He's had an eye on your land. I guess he thought I registered it."

A thought occurred to Bromley. "I never asked, but I know you've got no feeling for the slavers."

"I don't feel either way."

Bromley looked astonished. "You can't just stand in the middle. You've got to pick one side or the other."

"None of it's my fight."

Eli handed Dandy's reins to Bromley and walked into the general store. He bought cheese and crackers, and as an afterthought a ten-pound slab of bacon.

He came back and thrust the slab into his saddlebag. He split the cheese in town and gave half of it and some crackers to Bromley. They sat on the edge of the store's porch as they ate.

Bromley whittled a spot of mold from his cheese. He said earnestly, "This question has got to come to a head. A man's got to know where he stands. And the people around him got to know it."

Eli shook his head. Man was a quarrelsome animal. And he wasn't content being in a quarrel by himself; he had to pull everybody else in. He said, "Cass, I came out here to find my land. Thanks to you, I've found it. I've got to build a house and barn; I've got to break ground and plant. Show me where I have time for anything else. I'm against slavery, but I didn't start it, and I can't stop it. If they let me alone, I'll let them alone."

"They won't," Bromley muttered.

A man rode down the street and yelled, "Howdy, Cass. Brady got four kegs of beer in this afternoon."

Bromley's face brightened. He tossed the remaining bite of cheese into the street. "Damned dry cheese and crackers soaked up every drop in me. We're going to get some of that beer."

He took Eli's arm and led him toward the saloon. It was a bare, little room with a single table and a half-dozen chairs before a plank bar. The man behind it had a fat, jovial face and small, twinkling blue eyes.

"Eli, meet Daniel Brady. It's rare when a man can buy a glass of beer here. He drinks it all himself."

Brady wrapped a meaty hand around Eli's. His beaming face displayed broken teeth. "Don't believe anything he says. If you've known him very long, you know he isn't trustworthy."

Eli decided he liked the man. Brady looked ponderously slow and soft, but there was strength under that fat.

"You settling here?" Brady asked.

"Next to me," Bromley said. "He just registered with Murphy."

Brady murmured, "Haines isn't going to like that."

Bromley made an inelegant comment about what Haines could do. He said, "Draw us a beer, Dan. I know you got some."

Brady drew two mugs and scraped off part of the foaming head. "I waited a month for that freighter. And then he only brings me four kegs. If a few more Cass Bromley's drop in, it won't last two days."

Bromley emptied his mug without taking it from his lips.

"You see what I mean," Brady said.

Eli nodded. Maybe Lacey had a right to be concerned about Bromley stopping at the tavern. He drank from his mug. The beer was lukewarm, but it tasted good.

Brady was drawing another mug from Bromley, when he stopped. "Speak of the devil," he said in a low voice.

Eli turned his head. The man just coming through the doorway was of medium height and thin. He carried himself well, almost with arrogance. His cheekbones were high and prominent, and his restless, black eyes swept the room. He had a hawklike nose, and a haughty pride shone in his face. His clothes were expensive, and the black, calfskin boots were the finest money could buy. Eli never expected to own a pair of boots that good.

The newcomer said, "Brady, who owns that freak tied to the rack outside?"

A wicked grin rode Bromley's face. "Haines, you've just got to put your foot in it, don't you?"

Haines gave him a contemptuous glance. "Your horse, Bromley? I wouldn't be seen dead on something like that."

"My horse," Eli said evenly. "I expect to be seen on him."

Those black eyes swept Eli up and down. "You're new here." Haines made it a statement.

Eli couldn't resist the temptation to bait the man. "Why, no," he said soberly.

"I haven't seen you around," Haines persisted.

"That's funny. I've been here since yesterday."

Bromley laughed and slapped his thigh. A grin spread across Brady's face.

Twin spots of red mottled Haines's cheeks. "Another damned abolitionist, I suppose."

"Suppose what you want," Eli said shortly. He had felt dislike of Haines at first sight, and each word the man spoke deepened it.

"Get used to him, Haines," Bromley said. "He just registered the land next to mine."

Bromley's words made a visible impact on Haines. His mouth sagged, and the rush of his breathing pinched his nostrils tight. "You always led me to believe you'd registered all that land. Are you telling me that part of it was open?"

"Open as outdoors," Bromley said cheerfully. "I just drove in claim stakes. I never signed them or registered the land. If you'd step off your horse and get those fine boots dirty now and then, you might see what's going on."

Haines jerked his head at Eli. "Are you telling me you let him have that land?"

Bromley's drawl was a fair imitation of Haines's Southern accent. "You-all is having trouble undahstandin' tonight, ain't you-all, Mistuh Haines?"

Haines's eyes were malignant coals, looking enormous against their white background. His words were almost incoherent. "I won't forget this, Cass Bromley." His wild eyes took in Eli. "I'll remember you, too."

He stalked toward the door, stopped there, and said, "One of these days we'll run all of you abolitionists out of the country. They've already started in Atchison. A friend of mine told me yesterday about catching that abolitionist preacher, Silas Tracy. They burned an R on his forehead for Republican, then lashed him to a two-pole cottonwood raft and shoved him out into the Missouri River. I hope he drowned."

Muscle bunched in Eli's jaw. "He was an old man. How many of your kind did it take to subdue and tie him on that raft?"

Haines made a strangled sound, then turned and plunged out of the door.

Worry shadowed Brady's eyes. "You've made a bad enemy, Cass." He nodded at Eli. "And you, too."

"To hell with him," Bromley said. "Was that preacher a friend of yours, Eli?"

"No. He was an irritating old man. He kept at you until you thought he'd never stop."

Bromley's eyes held an odd look. "Well, he had a certain amount of bravery. He must have gone into Atchison and preached against those slavers."

"I have no doubt of it," Eli said curtly. This time Tracy had screamed at men who had respect for neither his age nor his cloth.

Bromley went back to his original subject. "That damned Haines grabs everything he can get his hands on. I've heard he's registered over a thousand acres already."

Brady said slowly, "It could be true. When a man gets land hunger—" He finished by shaking his head. "I'm telling you, he meant what he said."

"Give us another beer, and we'll drink on it," Bromley said carelessly.

"One's all," Eli said. Lacey was waiting for them. He didn't intend that Bromley spend the large part of the evening here, while Lacey worried.

He let Bromley finish his beer, then dragged him outside. Bromley complained about it all the way home.

Lacey met them at the door and said tartly, "You're back sooner than I expected."

Bromley pushed by her. "You can thank him," he growled.

Lacey did, with her eyes. Eli handed her the slab of bacon. "I remembered you were out of bacon."

"Cass wouldn't," she said. "You didn't have to do that."

"I'd like to stay here until I get my house built."

She smiled at him. "We wouldn't have it any other way."

"But only if I can pay my way."

"Don't argue with him, Lacey," Bromley said. He still rankled over their early departure. "He's hard-headed. Maybe a little faithless, too. He told me he's not on either side. Even the abuse of a friend of his doesn't move him."

Eli said sharply, "I told you he was no friend of mine. I met him on the boat. No more."

Lacey sliced bacon and dropped it into a pan. "What happened?"

"The slavers branded a preacher and tied him to a raft, then shoved him into the river."

"That's terrible," Lacey cried. She looked at Eli's stony face, and a touch of anger was in her eyes. "Can't you even feel pity for him?"

Eli's pity was watered by his anger. "Yes," he snapped. "But a man can't walk into another man's camp and criticize it without expecting to take the consequences." He locked eyes with Lacey, and sparks flew both ways. "As I told Cass, I'm against slavery. But I can do nothing about it. Such things as happened to Tracy will have to be handled by law."

Bromley sneered, "What law's here is on their side."

Eli went on stubbornly, "I came out here to take up land. To live my own life. I expect that privilege, and I'll give it." He stood and his face was stiff. "I guess it was a mistake asking to stay here."

"Sit down," Lacey ordered. "If we hadn't wanted you, we wouldn't have asked you. And Cass, you shut up. He's got a right to the way he feels."

Eli listened to the bacon sizzling in the pan. He looked about the room. These really were the only two people he knew well here. They were his bulwark against loneliness and homesickness. He muttered, "I'm sorry."

Bromley said gruffly, "I've got a big mouth. Lacey, are we going to have to wait all night for something to eat?"

They were at their bickering again. At first Eli had been disturbed to hear the acid comments that flew between them. Now he understood the affection behind those comments.

Lacey said one other thing along the subject. "Eli, I hope you can live your life the way you want to. But sometimes you have to fight for what's right."

Lane had said much the same thing. And Walker, too, Eli remembered. Was everybody in Kansas spoiling for a fight? Well, he was different. He would not be drawn into it.

Later, as he lay on his pallet, he thought about what Lacey had said. She had looked years older as she spoke. Trouble was no stranger to women. They shared in every bit their menfolk created.

CHAPTER TEN

In the morning Bromley asked, "Do you want to get started today?"

"Started on what?"

"Your house."

Eli's heart leaped. It was a generous offer, but he couldn't accept it. "You've got your own work."

"I'm pretty well caught up. But don't say no to me twice. I've worked lumber out of that bottoms. I know what it takes."

"Then I'll accept. If you take half of the lumber."

Bromley nodded. "A man never has enough."

They put an ax, a crosscut saw, files and rope into the wagon. Bromley hitched the team and said, "We'll need Dandy, too."

The closer they got to the river, the denser the timber grew. It looked like a massive, green wall, towering high overhead.

Bromley said, "There's a crick cuts through just ahead and empties into the river. A little temporary sawmill is at the mouth of the crick. We can float the logs there. You can pay the owner for the sawing, or he'll take half."

"How much is the sawing?"

"Ten dollars a hundred."

Eli debated briefly. It would be faster to pay for the sawing and take all the lumber. But that would make his house more expensive. He said, "I'll give him half."

Bromley nodded approval. A man was smart to conserve his cash resources.

The forest closed in around them. Ancient trees, some of them four feet thick at the butt, had fallen year after year, lapping and overlapping other fallen trees. A man would earn every foot of lumber he took out of here.

Bromley selected a spot a hundred yards from the creek. "I worked here a couple of months ago. I cut out a road to the crick. Look how the damned brush is already coming back."

It was hot in the timber. Young trees struggled for survival against the older ones, and if any ground space was left, the brush filled it. No air stirred in this thick, dense growth.

Bromley rolled up his sleeves. "Pick out your log."

Eli had his choice of hundreds of logs. Most of them were black walnut, thoroughly seasoned. They would make beautiful lumber.

He picked a three-foot log that was fairly free. He asked, "How many will we need?"

"How big a house do you want?"

Regulations called for at least twelve feet by twelve feet.

Eli wanted a bigger house than that. "I thought about sixteen by sixteen."

Bromley grimaced. "A few hundred more logs one way or the other will make no difference."

They sawed the jagged stubs of roots off the butt end. Bromley knew how to handle a saw. He threw it back at Eli, not riding his end, then drew it back toward him, putting weight on it so that the teeth bit deep. The musical whine of the saw was the only sound, and the clean smell of sawdust filled Eli's nostrils.

They made a second cut and an eighteen-foot log lay at their feet.

Eli grinned at Bromley and wiped sweat from his face.

"Don't look so happy over one log," Bromley growled. He slapped the back of his neck. "I thought they'd find us."

Eli saw a mosquito light on his forearm and killed it.

Bromley said, "If they get too bad, we'll have to build smudge fires." He grinned sourly. "You don't know what good working conditions are until you've worked in heat and smoke."

Dandy pulled the log to the creek bank, and Bromley said, "We'll roll them in all at once."

By noon they had to build their smudge fires, getting them started with dry wood, then smothering them with green leaves to produce the most smoke. The heat was rough, and Eli's eyes watered in the smoke. Bromley was right when he said they'd earn every log they got.

Eli's back was aching when they stopped for lunch. He flexed his hands, trying to work the soreness out of them. It had been a good morning's work. They had four logs on the creek bank.

Bromley squirmed his butt into a more comfortable position. He said, "We did all right." It was high approval. He had expected Eli to ask for quarter before the morning was over.

He opened the packet of lunch Lacey had fixed, and sighed.

"Bacon and corn bread again. Lord, a man gets tired of the same old thing."

Eli flew to Lacey's defense. "She didn't have anything else."

Bromley nodded. "She's a good kid. I couldn't have made it without her. We fuss a lot, but both of us would miss it if we stopped."

Eli knew nothing of Bromley's background, and he asked, "Where did you come from, Cass?"

"Pennsylvania. There's only Sarah and Lacey and me. We lost our folks when I was fifteen." His eyes were blank with old memories.

Eli's estimation of the man grew. Bromley had been pretty young when he took over the job of finishing raising two sisters. The memory of the struggle was in those blank eyes.

"Why did you come out here?"

"There's lots of good land in Pennsylvania, but we didn't have any of it. I guess poor land and poor folks just naturally go together. I figured we might as well starve out here as back there."

It was on Eli's tongue to tell him about Alicia. He couldn't name the reason, but he held the words. "I came from Ohio." He was lucky. He had a family to care for him. "It just got too crowded."

Bromley nodded his understanding. "If a man can stick out the first few hard years here, he'll wind up with something."

"I'll stick."

Bromley said, "I believe you will."

They finished their lunch and drank out of the creek. Bromley picked up his end of the saw. "This is a time when I could believe in slavery."

Eli smiled. He knew exactly how Bromley felt.

Eli's legs felt like rubber by the time the afternoon was over. He thought his hands were hard, but he had worn blisters on them. And his back was one huge, tender ache.

"That's enough," Bromley said. "It'll be close to dark by the time we get back."

"I saw some squirrels," Eli said. "How would a couple of them taste for supper? I put my rifle in the wagon."

Bromley's eyes gleamed. "Go get them."

It took twenty minutes for Eli to kill the two squirrels. He passed up three shots because the squirrels looked full-grown. A full-grown squirrel was usually tough.

He tied Dandy behind the wagon and climbed up beside Bromley.

Bromley said, "You handle that rifle good. I didn't see more than an eye of that last one you shot."

Eli patted the old rifle. "It shoots pretty true. What I'd really like to have is one of the new Sharps rifles."

Interest sparked Bromley's eyes. "I've heard about them. Is it as good as they claim?"

"I think it is. A friend of mine back in Ohio had one. I used it several times."

Bromley said, "I've heard rumors that a lot of them are being smuggled into Kansas."

"They'll make the difference. A few men armed with Sharps rifles could stand off a big number of men armed with the old weapons."

"Then I hope it's the free-state men getting them."

Eli changed the subject. "How long will it take to get the logs we need?"

"Three weeks." Bromley grinned. "Can you hold out?"

"I can hold out."

Eli wanted to write a letter to Alicia tonight. He wanted to tell her how well the house was progressing. He saw it in his mind's eye, a grand, imposing house, one that would make her gasp with delight when she saw it.

Bromley stopped the wagon before his house. "Go on in. I will skin the squirrels. You killed them. It's up to me to clean them."

Eli didn't realize he was so tired until he stepped down.

His legs buckled, and he grinned wanly at Bromley. "I know I've been someplace."

Lacey was slicing bacon, and Eli heard her say rebelliously, "I get so damned tired of bacon, bacon, bacon."

She heard Eli's step and turned.

He grinned and said, "That's pretty bad language."

"I don't care," she said defiantly. "If you'd lived around Cass Bromley as long as I have, you'd be using even worse."

"He's quite a man, Lacey."

A tiny smile touched her lips. "Don't you think I know it?"

Eli liked these people more every hour he was around them. He owed them a great deal. He'd have to find a way to repay them.

He asked, "Lacey, how do I send a letter?"

"Leave it at the general store. It might be picked up to-morrow, or in two weeks." She picked up her knife again. "Delivery is as bad."

"Don't slice any more bacon, Lacey. Cass will be in, and you'll see why."

He enjoyed being mysterious. She pointed the knife at him and advanced slowly. "Tell me or I'll cut your throat," she threatened.

His hands shot up, and he begged, "Don't do it, Lacey."

Bromley picked that moment to step into the house. He looked at them in astonishment and said, "What the hell's going on here?"

Lacey flushed and lowered the knife. "Eli and I were just playing."

Eli grinned. "She was going to make me tell what you were doing outside." He enjoyed the confusion in Lacey's face.

Bromley grunted. "Knowing her, I thought it was the real thing." He held up the two small, skinned carcasses. "What do you think of these for supper?"

They looked awfully small, Eli thought. He should have killed another one, at least.

"Eli got them," Bromley said. "Two shots, two squirrels."

Lacey wasn't forgiving her brother for putting that confusion in her face. "That's more than you could say."

"Yep," Bromley said cheerfully. "A squirrel has to look down the rifle barrel before I can hit him. We got something valuable in our new neighbor. He can give us a change from that damned bacon."

"Thank you, Eli," she said, and an odd radiance was in her eyes.

She fried the squirrels to perfection. And wonder of wonders, she set a huge bowl of fried potatoes on the table. "Mrs. Deloe was by this afternoon," she explained. "She gave me the last of her winter-stored potatoes. I had to cut away a lot of the sprouts. They aren't too bad, are they?" she asked anxiously.

"They're perfect," Eli said. He hadn't eaten fried potatoes in a long time. He hoped Mrs. Deloe kept on showing neighborly qualities.

With the potatoes and corn bread, the squirrels were more than enough. He felt drugged from the meal and fatigue. Bromley finished sucking on a bone. He said, "I won't have any trouble sleeping tonight."

Eli felt the same way. He wanted to put off writing that letter, but he would probably feel no better tomorrow night.

He waited until the table was cleared, then borrowed a sheet of paper and a pencil. He put down "Dear Alicia," and stared at the words. It was hard to get started. Bromley was half asleep in a chair, and Lacey was finishing the dishes. Lord, if he sat here staring at that paper another minute, his eyes were going to close.

He wrote rapidly, needing to get this letter behind him. He told her the house was progressing satisfactorily. He described its rooms, making it bigger than it was going to be. That was only a semi-permanent lie, for didn't he intend to enlarge it one of these days?

Lacey put away a dish and asked over her shoulder, "Are you writing to your family?"

He frowned at the interruption. "Yes." That wasn't a real lie, either. Alicia was going to be his family.

His longing for her surged upward in an overwhelming tide. He wrote how much he missed her, that he hoped to see her soon, and the earlier stiff words became fluid and eloquent.

"Are you going to tell them about me?" Lacey asked. The flashes of woman he had seen in her were completely gone. She looked like a child, anxiously seeking recognition.

He could imagine the reception his letter would get if he wrote Alicia about another girl.

"Yes," he said, and smiled. That was an outright lie, but it was a harmless one. He signed the letter, folded it and put it into his pocket. He was relieved that the chore was over. He would mail it the first opportunity he found.

CHAPTER ELEVEN

The house was taking shape. Bromley had refused any of the sawed lumber, saying, "You need it all now. I'll get mine out of you later."

"You'll get it back, Cass," Eli promised.

On Bromley's advice he had it sawed into two-inch planking. As seasoned as it was, it shouldn't shrink, and if cracks did appear, he could either batten or chink.

Eli had decided on posts, set in the ground, rather than rock pilings. Bromley jeered at him for fretting over the house being perfectly square, the corner posts being plumb.

He said, "You act like you're planning on bringing a bride into this house."

Eli was, though he had never told Bromley or Lacey about Alicia. He couldn't say why he hadn't. The right moment just never seemed to come along.

Bromley kept saying, "Slow down. She'll wait for you."

She had to wait. The intensity of the thought brought a desolate feeling to Eli, for its counterpart also popped into his mind. Suppose she didn't. That was a ridiculous worry. He had had one letter from her, six pages of finely-written script, saying how much she missed him. She wanted to come out right away, and he had refused in his answering letter. He wanted the house finished and a crop in the ground. Preferably, that crop should be sold, for the building was making a frightening dent in his money.

The hours from daylight to dark were filled with the sound of hammers and the whine of saws. The walls were up, and the general store in Trading Post had promised to order tar paper for the roof. If it didn't come within the next week, Eli planned to make a trip to Osawatomie to see if he could find it.

He had a qualm of conscience over the hours Bromley spent here, and Bromley said against his protests, "I'm caught up until wheat-planting time. You'd better get some in."

Eli wanted to, how badly he wanted it. But it depended upon finishing the house. Until it was done, he could break no ground, and he couldn't afford to hire it done.

The south end of the house was still open. Eli planned that the entire width of the wall would be taken up by a sod fireplace. Bromley approved of that. It would be quick to lay up, and it would heat the house in the winter.

Bromley said, "It went up as fast as any house I ever saw."

"Cass, you don't know how grateful I am."

Bromley made a crude remark, but his face showed how pleased he was. He took pride in this house, too. He said, "Another ten days should finish it. What are you going to do for furniture?"

"Make it."

That was a sound idea, and Bromley said, "It'll save you money."

Eli picked up his hammer. The brief respite was over. Before Bromley went back to work, he said, "We'll lose a day next week."

Eli frowned. An hour was precious, a day priceless. "What for?"

"Election day. You've heard talk of it in town."

Eli remembered he had. He just hadn't paid much attention. Bromley and the other settlers loved to gather at the general store, or Brady's saloon. They could waste an entire day with an aimless recounting of every little happening. It was rare that a newspaper reached down this far, and this was the only way they had of keeping up with the news. They talked about arguments between free-state and pro-slave men, of how a free-state man was knocked down last week. They were pretty unhappy when Eli didn't growl and curse the pro-slavery men. He just got up and walked away. He knew Bromley was telling those men that Eli disliked the slavers as much as any of them. Once, he heard Bromley say, "He's planning on getting married, you know. That keeps a man's head pretty busy."

Eli said, "I'd forgotten about the election."

"You believe in voting, don't you?"

"I believe in it," Eli snapped. But why would it take a whole day to ride into town and vote? He made up his mind it wouldn't.

The hard shine left Bromley's eyes. "Good. We've got to be careful about the men we elect to the legislature. They're going to make the laws we have to live with." His face was sober. "Its results are going to determine who controls Kansas Territory—free-state men or pro-slavery men. One thing for sure, pro-slavery men won't get many votes around here. Outside of Haines, I can't think of more than a half-dozen votes for them."

Eli said, "We can get in another hour of work before supper."

Bromley groaned and followed him.

Bromley hitched up the team early election-day morning.

Lacey came out, and she was dressed in her best. Her eyes shone with anticipation. She could spend the day visiting with the town womenfolk.

"Aren't you going in with us?" she asked Eli.

"I'll ride Dandy in. I might want to leave before you do."

He never did catch up with the wagon. A couple of times he saw the dust it raised, but no more. Bromley must be keeping the team at a pretty hard run.

The town was packed with people when Eli reached it, and most of them were strangers to him. He heard coarse jokes and laughter directed at his mount, and he kept his face wooden. He had seen this type of man before in Kansas City. Border toughs, Jim Lane called them. But what were they doing here this far south? Their presence worried him, and an uneasy thought crossed his mind. Had Tim Copple collected a bunch of his kind and come down here looking for him? As Eli rode down the street he cast uneasy glances from side to side, half afraid he would see the big man. He didn't miss the plentiful supply of jugs being passed from hand to hand. Right now the humor between these strangers ran high and rough, but it could turn mean.

Men kept pouring into town, men on horses and mules and in overcrowded wagons. Many of them were dressed in butternut breeches and red shirts. All of them carried rifles or side arms, and none of them looked like hard-working settlers.

Eli worried about this invasion of Trading Post. It was a small, poor town, and it held nothing of interest to this kind of man. He worried about Bromley and Lacey. The smart thing to do was to find them and get out of town as quickly as they could.

He decided it would be wisest not to leave Dandy on the main street. The best he could expect would be rough jokes and comments about the animal. At worst some of the toughs might try to abuse Dandy. Eli knew he wouldn't be able to take that.

He tied Dandy behind Murphy's shed and went looking
for Bromley. He found him behind Brady's saloon, talking
to Murphy and two other men he knew by sight.

He said, "I put my horse behind your shed, Murphy. I
didn't want to leave him on the street."

Murphy understood, for he nodded. "It's all right, Eli."

Eli turned to Bromley. "Cass, what's going on? What are
all these strangers doing in town?"

Bromley's face was bitter. "We've lost the election."

Was Bromley crazy? The election had hardly started, and
here he was talking about it being lost.

"Those strangers are Missourians, crossing the border to
vote in our election. The report is they were given a dollar a
day and free liquor to cast a vote. And you know how
they'll vote."

Eli said, "They can't vote. They're not residents of this
district."

Murphy smiled wanly. "That's what I tried to tell a couple
of them. I thought they were going to cut my throat."

"I say throw them out of town," Bromley said hotly.

"Use your head, Cass," Eli said sharply. "They outnum-
ber us a dozen to one. All of them are armed. How many of
our men brought guns into town?"

Murphy said, "He's right. It's a hard thing to swallow but
what else can we do? They're half drunk already and spoiling
for trouble. Stir them up, and they'll tear down the town."

Eli asked, "Cass, where's Lacey?"

"At Mrs. Hayworth's. All the womenfolk will stay indoors
this day." Mrs. Hayworth had a house in Trading Post. Lacey
should be safe there.

"It would be smarter to take her home."

"I will not leave," Bromley said furiously. He was in the
grip of a passion he could do nothing about. "The fraudulent
votes will carry the election in this district. They're probably
doing the same all over Kansas. They'll elect a pro-slave legislature, and they'll make the laws that rule us."

Eli shrugged. Bromley was probably right, but what could

any of them do about it? He felt a small, personal relief. Tim Copple wouldn't come this far to cast a vote.

He stuck close to Bromley during the next hour, for he knew the hot temper of the man. Bromley's indignation grew as the morning lengthened. He had a right to it, Eli admitted. He saw some of the Missourians vote a second and a third time, and none of the judges dared challenge them. Eli didn't blame the judges. It would have been suicidal to make any show of opposition. He could appreciate Bromley's anger, for it was beginning to burn in him. But he kept a tight grip on it. Anger was a useless thing unless a man could do something about it.

A half-dozen times he suggested that they leave, and each time Bromley shouted against it. "I will not leave. I've got a duty here."

"You've already voted," Eli pointed out. "What more can you do?"

"I don't know," Bromley said stubbornly. "But I'm staying."

Eli sighed inwardly. All he could do was to stay with Bromley, to keep him out of trouble if he could, to help him if he got into it.

They saw Haines a dozen times. Haines was in his glory. His pockets seemed inexhaustible when it came to buying drinks for the Missourians. The townspeople stood off to one side and hated him for it. It never touched Haines's satisfaction with himself and with the way the day was going.

He bumped into Eli and Bromley in the street and gloated, "We're winning. We'll whip you abolitionists into shape now."

Bromley's face was awash with anger. "Do you think these results will stand. We'll appeal in court."

Haines broke into laughter. "What court? The courts will be ours. You appeal and be damned."

He moved away, and Eli laid a hand on Bromley's arm to restrain him.

He said in a troubled voice, "Cass, you're not doing any good."

Bromley snarled at him, and Eli said, "I'll see you when you've cooled down a little."

He turned and moved toward Murphy's house. He would see how Dandy was doing. He was surprised to find he was angry—at himself, at Bromley, at the whole damned day.

He turned the corner of the shed, and a lank, black-haired man was walking around Dandy. He carried a bottle in one hand, and his unsteady walk showed that he already had had too much to drink. He wore the typical costume of the Missouri borderman, and Eli saw the pistol in its holster.

The man looked at Eli and said, "You tell me what this is."

Eli had had enough bad jokes about his horse. He said shortly, "You know what it is."

"But I don't believe it," the man said, and chortled. "I'm going to ride him down the street. The boys have got to see this."

"No," Eli snapped.

A hand dropped to the pistol butt. "I didn't hear you right, did I?" the man asked.

Eli smiled weakly. "No, you didn't."

"I thought not," the tough said.

He turned to put a foot in the stirrup, and Eli moved. He took a long stride and clamped a hand on a shoulder. He jerked, turning the man around, and cut off the startled squawk with the other fist. It was a good blow, with momentum and anger behind it. It landed on the man's chin, and he dropped.

Eli stood over him, breathing hard. The man didn't need another. Now Eli had no choice. He had to get out of town.

He untied Dandy's reins and mounted. He turned him and looked at the unconscious man. He saw him stir a little. In a few moments he would be coming to, and Eli would be smart if he put as much distance behind him as he could in those few moments.

He rode out of town without looking back.

He waited for Lacey and Bromley at their house, and it was after dark before they arrived.

The memory of the day was in Bromley's face and voice. He shouted, "Where'd you go? I looked all over for you." He kept working himself up, and he couldn't stop his words. "You've got a lot to learn. Every man has his personal problems. But he's got more than that, too. He's got a duty to the community he lives in. He's got their problems, too. He can't just run away and leave them."

Eli asked quietly, "Are you through?"

Lacey said sharply, "Let him talk, Cass."

Eli told them about knocking the man down. "I wasn't going to have Dandy abused. And I couldn't fight all of them."

Bromley said sheepishly, "Aw, I'm sorry, Eli. But I thought you just ran away and left us."

Lacey said shortly, "You always did talk too much, Cass." She walked into the house and slammed the door behind her.

"Eli, you're not sore?"

"No," Eli said. "Good night, Cass."

He mounted and rode away. He wasn't sore. Maybe a little resentful would be a better term for it. Something Bromley had said stuck in his mind. A community's problems were an individual's, too. He kept pushing at the thought, and it wouldn't go away.

CHAPTER TWELVE

The first winter was behind him and Eli waited impatiently for the planting season. He bought an old plow and scoured its share with a piece of sandstone until it was bright and gleaming. He put Dandy to work pulling the plow, and the horse sighed lugubriously with every step. But he was an honest horse. He put his full weight into the harness.

One brilliant, clear day faded into another. The southward slopes were red with wild strawberries. They were tiny things, no bigger than a man's little fingernail, but deliciously sweet. Before Eli finished the day's work he intended to pick a hatful for tonight's meal.

Wild flowers were everywhere, the straw-colored evening primroses vying with the bright yellow blossoms of the compass plant. Pink running roses splashed against the blue of the lupine. It was a shame that all this beauty had to be turned under, but a man couldn't live on beauty alone.

He plowed steadily through the day, and the warm, rich smell of turned earth filled his nostrils. He looked back at his work and was content. He had turned more earth in a day's time back in Ohio, but it hadn't been virgin soil.

He patted Dandy's neck and said, "You've earned supper, boy."

He picked his strawberries, unharnessed Dandy from the plow, and jumped on his back.

Bromley was waiting for him at the house. He said, "I got you your flour and sugar. I put them in the house."

"Thanks, Cass."

Bromley had time on his hands these days, and he spent a great deal of it in Trading Post. He had hired his breaking done, and it left him free until planting time. Eli didn't envy that free time. He was glad Bromley made frequent trips into town. It saved him the time he would lose in shopping.

Upon sudden impulse he thrust the filled hat at Bromley. "Maybe Lacey would like these."

Bromley looked at them sourly. "She's crazy about them. Always after me to pick her some. But they take so damned long to gather."

Eli laughed. Bromley was an impatient man with things that infringed upon his leisure hours.

He asked, "Any mail for me, Cass?" He received an occa-

sional letter from home, but it had been a long time since
he had heard from Alicia.

Bromley shook his head. He was still looking at the strawberries. "I'll take them, if you'll have supper with us."

Eli knew he should refuse. He was over there so often. He
contrasted his cooking with Lacey's. His cooking lost. He
said, "Lacey will get so she can't stand the sight of me."

Bromley said dryly, "You don't see very well, do you?" He
turned his horse and said, "About an hour?"

Eli nodded. He would need that much time to feed
Dandy and clean up.

He smelled the aroma of frying steak before he stepped
into the kitchen. My God, he had forgotten such smells still
existed.

Bromley laughed at the expression on his face. "Murphy
butchered a cow. She'd quit milking. I bought a quarter off
him. It'll probably be tough," he warned.

Lacey said crossly, "If it is, I'll shoot myself. I pounded it
until my arm was ready to drop off."

She watched anxiously as Eli took his first bite. It was a
little on the tough side but delicious.

He said, "It's wonderful."

Contentment replaced her anxiety at his praise.

She had mashed potatoes and spring greens to go with the
steak. Her eyes shone as she portioned out the strawberries.

"My first this season," she said. "Cass is always too busy
to pick them."

"I'll pick them for you as long as they last," Eli promised.

It was such a simple thing to do. He couldn't understand
the radiance in her eyes at all.

She sprinkled the berries with sugar, and Bromley said,
"These would be something with cream." He slapped the
table with his palm. "By God, next year, we're going to have
us a cow."

Lacey and Eli exchanged smiles. Cass Bromley was the best
promiser they knew.

Bromley said, "I picked up a lot of news in town today."

"Cass, don't you start any arguments," Lacey warned.

Eli grinned. "He can't get one out of me tonight. I'm too tired."

Bromley said, "Do you know those damned Missourians stole the election in fourteen out of eighteen voting districts?"

Eli said, "That's probably exaggerated, Cass."

Bromley said triumphantly, "Exaggerated, is it? I've got the paper to prove it. Murphy gave me his copy." He pulled a folded newspaper from his pocket and spread it out before Eli. "The *Kansas Free State*. Published at Lawrence." At Eli's frown he said, "Maybe you knew the town as Wakarusa. They changed it to Lawrence." Bromley's voice was filled with satisfaction. "Big things are happening around Lawrence, Eli. That's going to be the hub of our resistance."

Not mine, Eli thought. To have its own paper, Lawrence must have grown.

He scanned the story of the election, and a frown touched his face. If the newspaper story was true, the stolen election was a bad thing.

"Say you don't believe me now," Bromley challenged. "But that's the big news. Jim Lane made a speech at Big Springs. He calls the new legislature a bogus legislature, elected by fraudulent votes. That name will stick, Eli."

Eli nodded impatiently. He was interested in reading the account of Lane's speech, and Bromley's chattering interrupted him.

He finished the story and asked, "Do you approve of his speech?"

"He's a fighting man," Bromley said solemnly. "He's the man to lead us."

"Do you approve of the Black Law he proposed? That no Negro, slave or free, should be allowed to live in Kansas."

Bromley said, "I don't want any black son taking my land."

"Use your head," Eli said in disgust. "How could they do that? You're properly registered."

Bromley looked uncertain. "I don't know how. But Lane said it could happen. I believe him."

Eli said, "I wonder what he's after?"

"What do you mean. He's just doing a job that has to be done."

Eli shook his head. "He told me he had no interest but to live on his land in peace."

Bromley looked astounded. "You know him?"

"I met him. We were thrown together for a short time."

"What's he like?" Bromley asked eagerly.

Eli shook his head as he thought of Lane's mercurial moods. "I don't know," he said shortly.

"I'd like to meet him," Bromley said. "His speech made him just about the most powerful man in Kansas. He's the kind of a man I could follow."

"You're against slavery, aren't you?"

Bromley's eyes grew wary. When Eli changed the subject so abruptly, he was usually setting a trap. "Yes," Bromley said cautiously.

"You'll tell the outside world you're against it?"

"Yes," Bromley said again.

"But you don't give a damn about the slaves. You haven't even got enough room in Kansas to give them a home."

"I didn't say that," Bromley roared.

"But Lane did. And he's the kind of a man you want to follow."

"Damn it, Eli. You're always twisting my words around."

"You're like too many people, Cass. You listen to a man's words and believe them without knowing anything about him."

"You know all about Jim Lane?" Bromley challenged.

"No," Eli admitted. He doubted that Sam Walker, Lane's closest friend, knew all about him. "But until I know what's in his mind instead of what's on his tongue, I'm not blindly following him."

Lacey saw the heat in their faces. "Stop it," she ordered.

"You keep out of this, Lacey," Bromley said wrathfully.

Eli laughed ruefully. They had spoiled another evening for her. "She's right, Cass. We can't do anything about what's happening miles from us. Let's drop it."

"I know your way," Bromley said in a sulky tone. "You'd let anybody walk all over you."

Lacey gave Eli a fleeting smile. "I haven't seen much of that, Cass."

Bromley gave her a fierce glance. "You keep out of this."

Eli stood. Nobody could talk any reason to Cass Bromley tonight. "Thanks for the meal, Lacey," he said. "I'll see you tomorrow, Cass?"

Bromley sat in injured silence, and Eli sighed. It might be two or three days before Bromley wandered over. He would make some awkward remark about the work Eli was doing, and the argument would be over. Maybe we're too much alike, Eli thought wryly. Maybe we're too ready to prove to the other one how wrong he is.

CHAPTER THIRTEEN

A week later Judge Conley found Eli in the field. He looked at the straight furrows and said, "A good job, Eli."

"A slow job," Eli said, and laughed. "Dandy can't be hurried."

"It isn't a bad quality," Conley said thoughtfully. He was a thin, almost frail-looking man in his sixties. He had a fine-boned face with deep, thoughtful eyes. He had been a judge back east and had retired. Eli wondered what had driven him to this new, rough country. He respected Judge Conley. A half-dozen times he had seen men turn to the judge to settle an argument, and Conley had never given a hasty answer. Conley had some purpose in riding clear out here, and Eli waited.

"Have you heard the news?" Conley asked.

Eli smiled faintly. "Cass is always asking me that question. I don't hear much out here."

"Franklin Coleman shot Charles Dow in an argument over land."

Eli frowned. The names meant nothing to him. "It sounds to me like a private argument."

"Coleman is a pro-slavery man," Conley said. "Free-state men are saying he shot an unarmed man."

Eli wished Conley would get to the point. He couldn't see where the matter touched him at all.

"Sheriff Jones, the only recognized law around Lawrence—"

"Lawrence," Eli interrupted. "That's a long way from here. I don't see—"

"You might," Conley said calmly, "if you'd let me finish a sentence."

"Sorry, Judge," Eli muttered, and colored.

Conley's smile was forgiving. "Jones refused to do anything about arresting Coleman. Jones is also a pro-slave man. Coleman said it was self-defense, and two witnesses backed him up. Those witnesses got their houses burned."

Eli's frown deepened.

Conley smiled. "Just a minute. I'm coming to how it concerns you. Jones went to Lawrence to arrest the men who burned the houses. The people of Lawrence threw him out. Jones ringed Lawrence with a posse raised with federal approval. He claims the town will turn over the men he wants or he'll destroy it."

Eli's patience snapped. "I can't do a damned thing about it. Why tell me?"

"You can do something about it," Conley said calmly. "Cass is in town haranguing a bunch of men to ride with him to the aid of besieged Lawrence."

Eli stared at him, his mouth sagging.

"I tried to reason with him, but he wouldn't listen. And some of those he's talking to are as hot-headed as he is."

Eli exploded. "Why the crazy fool."

Conley's expression said he agreed with Eli. "He might listen to you," he pointed out.

"He will," Eli said grimly. He unfastened the plow and threw off the harness. He felt he didn't have time to go home and get a saddle.

He jumped on Dandy's back, and at Conley's surprised look he said, "I've ridden him bareback before."

He pushed Dandy as hard as he could; he even got a lumbering trot out of him.

He saw the crowd gathered in the street as he came down the hill toward Trading Post. Bromley was head and shoulders above the crowd, and as Eli drew nearer he saw that Bromley stood on a box. He could hear Bromley's voice a quarter-mile away though the words were indistinguishable.

Bromley was too busy yelling at his listeners to notice Eli's arrival. Eli dismounted at the edge of the crowd and pushed through it. He had to yell Bromley's name twice before he could interrupt him.

"Cass," he shouted. "How many men are going with you?"

Bromley swung around to face him, and for a moment, he looked startled. "Just about the whole damned town," he said.

A responsive roar from the crowd backed him up.

"You see?" Bromley asked triumphantly. An eagerness was in his eyes. "Did you come in to go with us, Eli?"

"How long ago did you hear the news, Cass?"

"Just this morning. A man rode through here and told us about it."

"How long was he on the road? Two, three days?"

Bromley frowned. "Maybe. What difference does it make?"

"You could be riding to help something that doesn't even exist any more. It could all be over."

The crowd no longer spoke with a concerted voice. Eli heard murmurs of individual talk among them.

"By God, Eli," Bromley yelled. "If you came in here to change our minds—"

"I came in here to tell you what damned fools you are. Do you know you'll be going against federal troops. Do you know Jones swore in all the bordermen he could find? Do you want to pull their attention to your town, your homes?" His voice grew more heated as he talked. "You're riding off and leaving your womenfolk unprotected. Suppose some of those toughs decide to ride in here while you're gone. You saw them here once. They could come again." He saw worried expressions beginning to appear among the crowd. "Cass, are you going off and leave Lacey alone?"

Bromley's eyes flickered, but he howled, "Don't listen to him. He doesn't give a damn what happens to Kansas."

Eli said flatly, "I care what happens to my land. And my neighbor's land. I can't protect any of it chasing around the country." His eyes challenged Bromley's. "Do you remember telling me I had a duty to my community? Where is that duty? Here—or at Lawrence?"

Someone called, "Cass, he's right."

A dozen voices raised in agreement.

Bromley had lost his listeners, and he knew it. "Listen to me," he shouted. "We've got to stop it there before it spreads here. We've got to—" He left the sentence unfinished. He had lost them. They were drifting away in small segments.

He jumped down from the box, and his face was furious. "Goddam you, Eli. One of these days, I'm going to have to whip you."

Eli said gravely, "It could come to that, Cass."

"Don't you ever talk to me again," Bromley raved.

He pushed by Eli and stalked toward Brady's tavern.

Conley gave Eli a sympathetic smile. "He'll get over it."

Eli's eyes were worried. "I don't know," he said. "I've never seen him so mad."

Conley threw his arm across Eli's shoulders. "Let's go buy him a drink and help him get over it." Admiration was evident in his voice as he said, "You did a masterful job, Eli. You used just the right arguments to reach them. You're a born leader."

Eli said ruefully, "I led myself right away from my best friend."

"I doubt it," Conley said cheerfully.

They stepped inside the tavern, and Bromley stood by himself at the end of the bar. Eli moved to him and said, "Cass, I'm sorry. I did what I thought was best."

Anger was unabated in Bromley's eyes. "Next time, leave me out of your damned thoughts."

"All right, Cass," Eli said in a low voice. "Forget it."

He moved back to Conley, his face wooden. But inwardly he was heartsick. One drink or a dozen wasn't going to mellow Cass today.

Bromley said in a loud voice, "If people had some guts, we could wipe out all this trouble."

Conley laid his hand on Eli's arm. The arm felt tense.

Bromley downed his glass and ordered another drink. He polished it off with a single gulp and extended the glass toward Brady.

Brady said, "Easy, Cass."

"Fill it," Bromley roared. "I've got enough people already trying to tell me what to do."

Brady shrugged and refilled the glass.

Eli stared bleakly ahead. Bromley intended getting drunk, and nobody could stop him. Eli looked at his balled fist. Damned if he wouldn't like to pound some sense into Cass's head.

Bromley finished his drink before Haines came into the room. Haines had been drinking heavily, too. It showed in the glassy shine of his eyes. He had a loose tongue when he was under the influence of whisky. Eli hoped Haines was smart enough not to say anything to Bromley.

Haines wasn't that smart. He lurched as he stopped at Bromley's side and grabbed at the bar for support.

"I heard your little speech out there," he sneered. "About chasing the pro-slavery men away from Lawrence."

Eli saw the cords bulge in Bromley's neck, and a slow red

crept up from his collar. Bromley clenched his glass very tightly. He was showing remarkable restraint.

"How many were going to follow you?" Haines asked. "Thirty? Forty?"

"Shut up," Bromley said in a low voice.

"Let's make it fifty," Haines said magnanimously. "Let's say fifty of them were no smarter than you."

Bromley put a glance on Haines. His eyes were wild. "I told you to shut up."

"Fifty rag-tails going up against federal troops." Haines laughed uproariously. "I can just see those troops running before you."

"By God, there's one way to shut you up," Bromley roared.

He whirled and swung, and it was a good blow. It landed on the hinge of Haines's jaw and knocked him back against the bar. He slid down its surface and lit in a sitting position, a dazed look on his face.

"Any of the rest of you want to argue about it?" Bromley asked.

He stared belligerently around the room, then stalked toward the door.

"He's really wild today," Conley murmured.

Eli nodded. He was watching Haines. The man's face was beginning to clear, and a murderous look was filling his eyes. He dug in his pocket and as his hand rose from it Eli saw the shine of metal in it.

Bromley was almost to the door as Eli yelled, "Look out, Cass. He's got a gun."

His warning seemed to freeze Bromley. Bromley turned, but he made no further move.

Eli took three, quick strides toward Haines. The gun was aimed at Bromley as Eli swung his boot. The toe thudded into Haines's hand just as the report of the gun sounded. Eli knew a heart-stopping moment. He might have been too late to destroy Haines's aim.

He saw the gun fly out of Haines's hand and skid across the floor before he looked at Bromley.

Bromley gaped at the freshly gouged splinter in the door-jamb, less than ten inches from his head. He stared at it a long time as though it were impossible for him to understand what had happened.

He turned his head slowly and stared at Haines. "He tried to kill me," he said in an unbelieving voice.

Rage rolled across his face, and he yelled. "Why the sneaking bastard."

He ran across the room, his boot heels pounding hard against the floor. He left his feet when he was six feet from Haines and dived at him.

A shoulder slammed into Haines's face, driving the back of his head against the bar. The impact took the breath and most of the resistance from him. His hands clawed feebly at Bromley, but there was no real strength in them.

Bromley's arms closed about him, and he rolled Haines out onto the center of the floor. He came up on top, and he slugged blow after blow into Haines's face. After the second one there was no movement from Haines. Bromley's rage still wasn't satisfied.

He sat on Haines's chest and grabbed an ear in each hand. He raised the head and pounded it against the floor. He repeated it over and over.

Conley reached him first. He grabbed his shoulder and said, "Man, you'll kill him."

Eli was on Conley's heels, and he said grimly, "It might not be a bad idea."

But he helped Conley pull Bromley off the unconscious man.

Bromley struggled against their hands, and his face was insane.

Eli was afraid he would have to hit Bromley to bring him back. "Cass, Cass," he kept yelling. "Look at him. He's out."

Something got through to Bromley, for he shook his head hard. When he looked at Eli again his eyes were clearing. He looked at Haines's ruined face and muttered, "He won't forget that for a long time."

"He won't," Eli said curtly. But he meant it differently than Bromley did.

Bromley's eyes were back on Eli's face. He made several false starts before he could speak. "You saved my life, Eli," he said huskily.

"I debated about it," Eli said, and grinned.

Bromley grabbed his hand, and Eli felt the hard pressure. "Eli, I'm a hot-headed fool."

Eli's grin broadened. "Weren't you always?"

"Don't fun me," Bromley said earnestly. "I don't know how to make it up."

"Don't try. Hadn't we better be going home? Lacey will be worrying."

Bromley said soberly, "I think it's a good idea."

He started for the door, and Eli asked, "What do you want to do about him?" He pointed at Haines.

Bromley shrugged. "Let him lie."

Eli felt it was a mistake. But Trading Post had no sheriff, no jail. He didn't know what to do about Haines either, short of killing him.

CHAPTER FOURTEEN

By the middle of October, Eli had twenty acres of ground broken and his wheat planted. He was content with his progress, and only one thing marred his satisfaction. He hadn't gotten a letter from Alicia. He had written three times and hadn't received an answer. He knew the fault wasn't hers. It had to be the mail's, and he cursed the service.

He came in from the field that evening, his face jubilant.

He had found the first tiny, green shoots marching in sol-
dierly lines the length of the field.

He washed his face and hands and changed to a clean shirt.
He debated upon taking a bath, but the October evening was
chilly. He decided he hadn't done enough hard work today
to warrant a bath. He was taking supper again with the
Bromleys, and he looked forward to it.

He went out to saddle Dandy, thinking that this was the
third invitation this week. He wondered if he was making
a nuisance of himself. These evenings were always pleasant if
he could keep Bromley off the subject of politics. Bromley
had a new hero—Jim Lane—and he was forever talking
about him. He gave Lane full credit for saving Lawrence
from the posse's siege, and Eli had pointed out a dozen times
that the crashing storm had saved Lawrence, driving Jones's
posse into disorganized rout. From all accounts it must have
been a tornado, battering Jones and his men, until the only
thought in their heads had been to save themselves. But
Bromley insisted the credit was Lane's. By mutual consent
they agreed not to talk about it again.

He walked into Bromley's house, and the place was filled
with good smells. Lacey smiled at him from the kitchen
stove and said, "Supper in fifteen minutes. Cass is out getting me some more wood. That man!" Her tone was tinged
with exasperation. "I told him this morning I didn't have
enough to last the day. And he spends all afternoon in Trading Post."

Bromley came in, his arms burdened with sticks of stove
wood. "Laziest white woman that ever lived," he grumbled.
"Can't even get herself a few pieces of wood."

Lacey said tartly, "If I did, next you'd want me to be split-
ting it."

"Wouldn't hurt you any," Bromley retorted. "It might fill
out that scrawny frame."

Eli didn't think she looked so scrawny. There had been an
amazing change in her the last few months. She seemed to

have grown more mature, and rarely did he see the flashes of girl-child. He thought soberly, Lacey's growing up.

Lacey threatened her brother with a handled pot, and Bromley said, "She'd throw it, if you wasn't here."

"Eli's going to throw you," Lacey said, "if you don't give him his letter."

Eli's heart bounded. The long-awaited letter from Alicia had arrived. He tried to keep the frown from his face as Bromley searched through his pockets.

"Did I lose the damned thing?" Bromley muttered.

Eli's fingers itched with the desire to choke him.

Bromley found the letter in his hip pocket and handed it to Eli.

Eli didn't realize the disappointment stamping his face as he stared at the familiar writing. It wasn't Alicia's.

He said, "It's from my family."

He opened the letter and scanned it rapidly. They were all well and settled down for the winter. He could shut his eyes and see the scene. The barrels were filled with apples and salted pork, and great stone crocks were crammed with sauerkraut. The fruit closet's shelves were lined with jars of canned fruit and vegetables. The mow of the barn was filled with sweet-smelling hay, and a mountain of cut and split wood was behind the back door.

Lacey asked, "Is something wrong?"

Eli frowned. "No. Why?"

"You had such a funny look on your face."

"Did I?" He supposed it was composed of a feeble remnant of homesickness, but mostly it was disappointment. He saw Alicia in every line his mother wrote, even though his mother didn't mention her. He couldn't remember his mother mentioning her for some time now.

Lacey said, "I'll bet your family's nice."

Eli nodded abstractedly. The next time he wrote he was going to ask some pointed questions about Alicia—and he wanted them answered.

Bromley asked sourly, "Are we out of the habit of eating?"

Lacey flushed. "It'll be on the table in a minute."

It was one of the best meals she had ever prepared. Eli stuffed himself on fried apples, sweet potatoes and squash. He had his choice of rabbit, squirrel or prairie chicken. And for dessert Lacey set a huge pumpkin pie on the table.

Eli ate his second piece of pie and groaned. "I hurt. Cass, after a meal like this I'd be sure I never offended her again."

Lacey's eyes danced.

He settled back in his chair, wishing he could loosen his waistband. He remembered the first scanty meals he had eaten in Kansas. Yes, life was getting better here.

Bromley said solemnly, "We're going to have to fight for the privilege of keeping on eating like that."

He shook his head at Eli's frown. "You can stick your head in the sand just so long. Then you got to pull it out to look around."

"I thought we'd agreed not to argue about it any more."

"I'm just trying to tell you what I heard in town."

Lacey listened eagerly. Any news was welcome to her.

Bromley said, "We got a new constitution, Eli. It was all settled in Topeka."

The new constitution had no official standing. The free-soil men had met in Topeka and in defiance of Governor Shannon had elected their own man. They called him governor, but he had no official standing.

Despite his intention not to listen, Eli grunted, "Who's going to recognize it?"

"I am for one," Bromley said heatedly. "Charley Robinson's been elected governor."

Eli knew that.

"I'll bet Jim Lane loves that."

"You don't like Lane, do you?"

"I didn't say that."

"You sounded like it. And after all he's done for Kansas."

"What?"

"Well, he saved Lawrence."

"Oh, my God," Eli said wearily. "We've been over all that

before. He didn't save Lawrence. He just grabbed credit for it."

Bromley stood. "If that's all the gratitude you've got for people who fight for you, I don't want to talk to you."

"That suits me," Eli said evenly.

Lacey cried, "You two act like a couple of children."

"I'm sorry, Lacey," Eli apologized.

Bromley wouldn't say he was sorry. He wouldn't even look at Eli.

Eli said, "It was a wonderful meal, Lacey."

She followed him outdoors. He took her hand and smiled at her. "Don't fret about it. He'll get over it."

"You two make me so damned mad," she said. "You can't talk politics without getting into an argument."

Eli was tempted to explain how he felt, then he laughed ruefully. "You're right, Lacey. I promise I'll never talk politics to Cass again."

"He'll be ashamed of himself in the morning, Eli."

"Sure," he agreed, and smiled. "I'm going to Osawatomie in the morning to see if the stump puller I ordered came in. Tell him I'll be happy for him to come along."

She squeezed his hand. "I will, Eli."

He dawdled over breakfast the next morning, waiting for Bromley to appear. He put his trip off an hour longer than he intended, waiting for him. He was half angry as he saddled Dandy. Lacey was wrong. Bromley wasn't ashamed of himself this morning.

By mid-morning Haines was drunk. He was drunk very often before noon these days. Each time he looked in a mirror and saw his misshapen nose, he felt like reaching for the bottle. He cursed Cass Bromley each time he saw it, and his hatred for the man lay in his stomach like a sour, heavy knot. Someday he would pay Bromley back, and savoring the thought kept him going. But he had two of them against him, for Eli Dryden would back Bromley. Any move against Bromley would be a move against Dryden, and the thought restrained Haines with a sly caution.

He made his trips to town as infrequent as he could these days. For he was certain he saw laughter in men's eyes each time they looked at his face. He cursed Bromley again in a silent, vicious tirade.

His eyes narrowed wickedly. Cass Bromley was driving his wagon into Trading Post, and he was alone.

Haines watched Bromley pull up before Siegman's general store and climb down. Bromley walked inside, and Haines stood for a moment in indecision. God, how he hated the man. He wouldn't draw a contented breath again until Bromley was dead.

He admitted his fear of Bromley, but his hatred drove him on. He walked toward the store with no definite purpose in mind. But this time, if an argument developed Eli Dryden wasn't around to protect his friend.

He stepped inside the store, and a pile of gleaming hatchets was displayed on a table in the center of the room. He moved to the table and picked up one of the hatchets. He ran his thumb over its edge.

Bromley was talking to Siegman, and he didn't see Haines come in. But Siegman did, and his eyes turned uneasy. He shifted his position as though trying to warn Bromley, and Haines glared at him.

Bromley finally caught Siegman's uneasiness and turned his head. He gave Haines a raking glance and said with cruel amusement, "I thought something important was bothering you, Sieg."

He turned back, and fury choked Haines. All right, he thought. You wait, Cass Bromley. He wished Siegman wasn't here. Then he'd do something about Bromley.

Bromley said, "Sieg, did you know that goddamed Pierce has acted against us? He's called the free-state government illegal and an act of treason. I'll bet that damned Southerner, Jefferson Davis, talked him into it."

"You watch what you're saying," Haines shouted. Twin spots of color were burning in his cheeks.

Bromley ignored the outburst. "I never knew a Southerner who wasn't good at talking—and nothing else."

"I told you," Haines said wildly. His collar felt too tight, and his head felt as though it were about to explode.

"Yes, sir," Bromley said, enjoying himself. "All talk and a yellow belly. That's a Southerner for you."

He looked over his shoulder at Haines and asked, "I'm not saying anything that offends you, am I, Haines?" He turned back to Siegman and said, "I wouldn't want to offend him. Not an honorable backshooter like him."

Queer noises were screaming inside Haines's head. This man had beaten and humiliated him. How much was a man supposed to take? He stared at the back of Bromley's head, and it seemed to grow bigger and bigger. He looked at the hatchet he still held, and for a moment, his eyes were blank and uncomprehending. Slowly they filled with an insane, red glare.

He shouted, "Goddam you," and rushed at Bromley's back. Siegman saw his face and the upraised hatchet. His face seemed paralyzed as he fought to find his tongue. "My God," he shouted. "Cass, look out."

Bromley tried to whirl, but the move was started too late. Haines brought the hatchet's edge down in a savage stroke against the back of Bromley's head.

It made a monstrous sound. It sounded like a club smashing against an overripe melon. Bromley cried out, took a broken step, and plunged forward on his face. The blade remained in his head, and the blood spurted around it.

Siegman's face was chalky, and his lips were palsied. He stared at Bromley with wide, horror-stricken eyes, and he looked as though he was going to faint. He clutched the edge of the counter for support and shook his head several times. When he raised it, his eyes were clearer.

He said, "You're a dead man, Haines. They'll hang you for that."

His words broke Haines's fascinated staring at Bromley. It had all been so simple—just one, little stroke, and it was all over. After the weeks of brooding about it, Bromley would never insult him again.

Siegman shrank back before the maniacal glare in the man's eyes.

"Nobody's going to touch me," Haines said, and ran for the door.

Two or three minutes passed before Siegman dared follow him. He ran outside and looked up and down the street. Haines wasn't in sight.

"Help," he shouted. "Haines just killed Bromley. Help."

Eli returned home late in the afternoon. His trip had been fruitless, and the waste of time made him tired and angry.

It grew dark much earlier now, and the shadows of the trees were stretching across the fields. Eli's thoughts were dulled by fatigue, and he was almost to his house before he realized that dark patch of shadow had moved. He heard the stomping of a horse and a man's voice, pitched too low to catch the words.

The dullness dropped away, and he called, "Who is it?"

"That you, Eli?" a voice replied. "We been waiting a hell of a long time for you."

As he drew nearer Eli saw that four horsemen were before his house. But the tenseness was gone. He had recognized Kenmore's voice. It was as big as the smithy's frame.

He joined them and asked, "What's the matter?"

They looked at each other, and some kind of constraint held them.

"Come on, come on," Eli said impatiently.

Kenmore sighed and said, "I guess one of us has got to tell you. Haines killed Cass. Killed him right in Siegman's store with a hatchet."

Eli heard the words; he understood them. But for a moment they filled his head with a meaningless sound, an unbelievable sound. He could feel the hurt swelling inside him and crowding up into his throat until he felt choked. His voice sounded like a low groan as he said, "No."

"It's true," Kenmore said with a ponderous wag of his head.

His words were difficult and awkward. "I don't have to tell you how all of us feel."

Eli's eyes were unseeing. He remembered a man standing in knee-deep water trying to get a team and wagon out. That hadn't been so long ago, but so close and satisfying had been his relationship with Cass that it seemed he had known him all his life. Cass Bromley, who hollered to hide his inner softness; Cass Bromley, who was always ready to drop what he was doing to help out a friend.

The loss was a knife slashing through Eli's guts, and the pain seemed unbearable. His eyes were hot and stinging, and his hands were so tightly clenched they ached. Something wet touched his cheek. His eyes were spilling over.

Kenmore placed an awkward arm across his shoulders. "I know how you feel."

He didn't know how Eli felt. No one could know—unless it was Lacey. He wished Kenmore and the others would leave him. He would be bawling like a baby in a moment.

He turned his back on them, and they didn't intrude on the poor bit of privacy. The rip tide of sorrow ran wild and unchecked for a long moment leaving him drained and empty.

Something had to fill that emptiness, and a cold and deadly anger laced through the grief. He wanted to curse God for letting men like Ross Haines walk the earth, but that would do no good.

He faced Kenmore and asked, "Where's Haines?"

"He ran," Kenmore said. "He ran real fast. You know that mare of his—" He made a helpless gesture, letting it finish for him.

He saw the raging criticism in Eli's face and said patiently, "By the time Siegman got the news to us and we got mounted up it was too late. We never came in sight of him. We tracked him some twenty miles south, then lost him." He finished with quiet dignity, "We didn't give up easy."

Eli knew that country to the south. It was big and wild. A lone man with a start and on a fast horse could easily lose himself.

"I know you didn't," he said, and heard Kenmore's sigh.

Eli's mother used to say, "All first grief is selfish. You think only of yourself, of what you've lost. The only cure is thinking of others."

Eli turned from self grief to the thought of somebody else. He asked, "Does Lacey know?"

Brady answered, "I guess she does, Eli. There's a lot of people at her house. We wanted to tell you before you saw her." He released a long, sighing breath. "This is going to be hard on her."

Eli's face was set tight. Nobody knew just how hard it was going to be.

As they moved toward Bromley's house Kenmore said, "Maybe Cass was right. Maybe you ought to stomp on people like Haines the minute you see them."

Eli said savagely, "I wish I had the opportunity to stomp on him now."

The yard was packed with horses, wagons and buggies, and Kenmore said, "I guess just about everybody's here."

Eli nodded and dropped Dandy's reins. He dreaded to see Lacey, dreaded to see the crushing hurt on her face.

The door opened, and Lacey was silhouetted by the lamp behind her. "Eli," she cried. "Is it you?"

She rushed out of the house, and he opened his arms. She flew into them and buried her face against his chest. She cried so hard he couldn't understand a word she was trying to say. He patted her shoulder and said, "No, Lacey. No." His cheeks were wet again.

She lifted her tear-ravaged face. "Cass is dead."

"I know, Lacey."

"I killed him," she sobbed. "I killed him."

He said sharply, "Stop that." Had the loss touched her mind?

"I did," she insisted. "I nagged at him all morning because he wouldn't tell you he was sorry. I nagged him so much he said he was riding into town to find some peace."

He pushed her away until he could see her face. "That's

crazy talk, Lacey. I could be blaming myself the same way. I argued with him. If I hadn't, he'd have gone with me. You can't tear yourself to pieces trying to figure out why it happened. It just did. Maybe I should have listened to him more. I don't know. I always thought the best way was to avoid trouble. But maybe Cass was right. If you rush in and grab hold of it first maybe it can't hurt you so much."

She stared at him, her eyes brimming with tears. She saw the intensity of his grief, and it laid a soothing hand on her own.

"None of it was your fault, Eli," she cried. "None."

His sigh was long and heavy. "I hope not," he muttered.

Mrs. Deloe bustled up her ample form, shaking with the effort of movement. "Poor little thing," she clucked. "I'll take her home with me."

Eli saw refusal forming on Lacey's face. He said, "Go with her, Lacey. Just for tonight." He didn't want her alone in this house with all the crushing weight of the memories.

He thought he might have trouble with her, but she went meekly enough. She looked back at him, and he gave her a faint smile.

He stepped inside the house and walked to the fireplace. He pulled a pistol from its niche behind the chimney. Cass was proud of that gun. He had showed it to Eli several times.

Eli looked at the people in the room, then dropped the pistol in his pocket. He said, "I'll never be without it from here on."

Kenmore guessed at his thoughts. "If you're thinking of Haines, it won't do you any good. He's clear out of the country by now, and he won't come back."

"He'll come back," Eli said. He was as sure that he would see Ross Haines again as he was that he would never see Cass.

CHAPTER FIFTEEN

Lacey insisted upon returning to her house after Cass's funeral. "This is my home," she answered Eli's objections to her being alone. "Where else would I go?"

He didn't argue against the set stubbornness in her face. But he tried to look after her needs. The heap of fireplace and stove wood behind the house was never allowed to dwindle, and he brought her fresh game whenever he could find it.

She appreciated what he did, but her smile wasn't the same, and he wondered if the old smile would ever return.

He finished harnessing the team as Lacey came out of the house. She was too thin, and it made her eyes look enormous.

"Did you eat last night?" he asked sharply.

"Yes," she said indifferently.

She ate when he was around, but he couldn't spend every hour of his time here.

He helped her into the wagon and tucked a blanket around her knees. It was mid-March but still chilly. In protected spots, patches of snow remained. But the promise of coming spring was in the air. The sun had strengthened its chilly illusion of warmth, and the wind was softening and losing its bite.

Lacey used to chatter endlessly before Cass died, but now it was difficult to get a sentence out of her.

He said, "It'll soon be planting time again."

She nodded without speaking, and he felt helpless against the wall she had built around herself.

He fell into his own brooding thoughts. He had had one brief note from Alicia, unsatisfactory and telling him nothing. He had replied in frantic haste, asking what was wrong, and she hadn't answered him. He saw now that he had been foolish, that he should have brought her with him, despite the hardships. Other families came and survived, and he and Alicia could have done the same, but he had wanted everything right for her. He thought with determination that when spring really came, he would go to Ohio and bring her back. But there was another problem. He had Lacey to consider. He couldn't leave her alone for any length of time.

He was scowling as he drove into Trading Post. Its one street was filled with traffic. It always was on Saturday. Saturday was the week's shopping day.

He tied the team before Siegman's store. "I'm going to the tavern."

She nodded. She never argued with him about it as she had with Cass.

He strode into Brady's, and the place was filled. Brady looked with a welcome smile and said, "Eli."

Kenmore said, "I was by Haines's house this morning. It still looks deserted."

Eli felt his face go tight. It always did at the mention of Haines. But he said calmly enough, "He'll be back." He knew it with a deep-seated conviction. Some day, he would see Ross Haines again.

Brady poured a glass of whisky and shoved it forward. "It'll take the chill out of your bones. We were just discussing the latest news. I heard Sheriff Jones went into Lawrence again to arrest a free-soiler."

"Did he make it?" Eli asked.

Brady grinned. "A man named Tappan punched Jones in the face. Then the people of Lawrence ran Jones and his posse out of town."

Eli said with wry humor, "Lawrence must be getting to be Jones's favorite town." This was twice, that he knew of, that Lawrence had humiliated Jones.

He said slowly, "I'm betting he won't let it drop. He's got President Pierce behind him now. He'll go in next time with the army behind him."

He saw faces darken, and shrugged. "He's got the law behind him."

Kenmore said savagely, "Then I say to hell with the law."

Eli eyed him quizzically. "Are you ready to fight the United States? That's about what it'll amount to now."

He left them with that disturbing question to argue over. He stepped outside, hoping that Lacey had finished her shopping.

He saw her come out of Siegman's store, her arms laden. He hurried down the street to relieve her of her packages.

He took the packages from her and placed them in the wagon. He started to climb into it, and she said, "Mr. Siegman gave me a letter for you." She pulled it out of her coat pocket and handed it to him.

His heart leaped as he saw the familiar, beloved handwriting. He glanced at Lacey, and she stared straight ahead. Did her stiffness have something to do with the letter? It might. She knew his mother's handwriting, but to the best of his knowledge she had never seen Alicia's. Did she guess it came from another woman? Was that the cause of her mood. He thought irritably, If all those questions are answered by a yes, what difference does it make to her?

He had to read the letter right now, and he said, "Excuse me, Lacey."

He walked to the back of the wagon, glanced at Lacey, then tore open the letter. His heart thudded at a fearful rate. Alicia would have a logical reason for her long silence.

His eyes galloped along the first few lines, then froze. He couldn't be reading right. His eyes had to be playing him tricks. He went back to the beginning, and his hands trembled.

"*Dear Eli:*" he read. "*This is the hardest letter I ever tried to write. Each week I knew it had to be done, and still I put it off. I was married three weeks ago to John Stipes. He is a fine man and while you were gone I found out how much I loved him. I'm sure you wish us well. Under the circumstances I think it best you do not write again. I'm sorry.*"

She signed it, "*Affectionately, Alicia.*"

He reread it again before the full import sank in. He cursed John Stipes, and he cursed Alicia. If there was only something he could get his hands on, something he could rend and tear. If he had only one wish in the world, he would wish Stipes was facing him.

The wild need of violence passed, and something hot and stinging pushed up behind his eyes. He kept a tight control; he would not allow himself to cry. She was fickle and faithless; she was not worth tears.

He tore the letter into tiny pieces and threw them into the air. He watched the wind scatter them. There went his dreams, his plans, his work and privations, scattered and lost by a puff of wind. A man's life crumbled just that easily.

Lacey hadn't looked around, and he was grateful she hadn't seen his display of emotion. He wished he didn't have her on his hands. He would like to walk into Brady's and drink as much whisky as was necessary to blot out the memories. Instead he had to take Lacey home, and the memories would be devils, stabbing at him with long, hot needles.

He sat down beside her, and she asked quietly, "Did you get bad news?"

He was too filled with words of protest, and some of them had to come out. "It was from the girl I was going to marry."

He didn't see the stillness grip her face and the light in her eyes die.

"Do you want to hear a funny ending to all my work and hopes?" he asked. "She married John Stipes." He laughed harshly. "John Stipes. Isn't that funny?"

The light returned slowly to her eyes. She rode a way in silence, then said, "If you weren't so wrapped up in your grieving, you'd see how lucky you are."

"Lucky?" he yelled at her.

"Yes, lucky. A woman who won't wait for a man isn't worth his grief."

He glared at her. "Shut up," he bellowed. "Will you just shut up?"

CHAPTER SIXTEEN

Lacey didn't speak to him again on the trip home, and the desolation swept back in on Eli. Nobody could have told him that time would ease the ravage of the letter. He would have called him a liar.

It would be dark, he thought dully, by the time they arrived home. He had planned for tomorrow to be a busy day, but it didn't matter now.

The team pulled up a hill, and Lacey seized his arm. "Eli," she cried. "Look!"

The terror and anguish in her voice jerked up his head. He saw the wavering spot of radiance a half-mile ahead and knew immediately what it was. Not too long ago that had been a big fire, and now it was dying for lack of fuel. A house had stood where that fire was—Lacey's house.

He pounded the team savagely with the whip, though he knew it was too late to save anything.

He pulled up and jumped down. He couldn't approach too closely, for there was still heat in the ashes. Where a house had stood was now only dying embers. An errant breeze stirred them, fanning them into a brief, new life, and the sparks danced skyward.

Lacey's face was cold marble. He stared at that blank face, and he feared for her sanity. He took her arms and shook her. "Lacey," he said sharply.

Her face crumbled, and the tears came. He let her cry, knowing she needed its release.

Her crying subsided to sniffles and hiccuping. "Everything's gone now," she said dully. "I hate this Godforsaken land."

"It's not the land, Lacey," he said quietly. "It's the people in it." A hard core of fury was lighted in him, and he could feel its spreading heat. He could name the man who did this as surely as though he saw him apply the torch. Ross Haines did this. What other man hated Cass Bromley enough to fire the house over his sister's head? A savage elation leaped through Eli. Haines was back, and this time Eli would find him.

He said, "Wait here," and moved toward the small shed behind the house site.

He had ridden Dandy over here this afternoon and left him tied in the shed. The sight of the unburned shed put a quick fear in him for the horse.

He looked in the shed, and a tremendous rage almost blinded him. Dandy was on the shed floor, his ungainly body looming bulky and grotesque. He had been shot through the head, and to Eli it was additional proof that Haines had been here. No other man would commit this senseless, wanton destruction.

He knelt and traced a finger down the stiffened shoulder, and he couldn't swallow around the hard, choking lump. He wouldn't tell Lacey about this—not now, for she had loved patient, plodding Dandy almost as much as Eli had.

He straightened and went back to Lacey. She was too shaken by her loss to notice the expression on his face.

He said, "Come on, Lacey," and led her back to the wagon. She asked dully, "Where are we going?"

"To my place."

Even before he saw the duplicate glow ahead of him he had known the trip would be futile. He stopped the wagon and stared at the distant red eye of light. He thought of all the hours of toil that had gone into the house, the hope, the love. All wasted. This day seemed to have been picked to show him the waste of his life.

Lacey covered her face with her hands, and he heard her racking sobs. She seemed to be taking the destruction of his house harder than her own.

It was useless to drive closer. He would find no more to salvage at his house than he had at hers.

He turned the wagon around. "We're going back to town, Lacey."

If she heard him she gave no sign. She sat listlessly beside him. His anger was still with him. He thought he would live with it for a long time; he wanted to live with it.

He drove into Trading Post and stopped the wagon before Judge Conley's house. The judge came to the door and peered into the darkness.

"Is that you, Eli?" he called.

"Yes," Eli replied.

Conley hurried outdoors, concern riding his face. Something had to be wrong. Eli had returned too soon.

"Somebody burned us out, Judge. My house and Lacey's."

Conley sucked in his breath. "Do you think you know the man?"

"I do," Eli said flatly. "It was Haines's work."

"Did you see him?"

"Nobody saw him. But I know."

Conley's face was troubled. "It's little to go on, Eli."

Eli's voice was too calm. "He'll tell me about it, when I find him. Will you take Lacey in?"

"Of course." Conley helped Lacey down. "Melinda," he called.

Mrs. Conley came to the door, and Conley said, "They burned Lacey and Eli out."

Outrage stamped her face. She put an arm around Lacey and said, "Come in, my dear." She shook her head at her husband. "There are devils abroad in this land."

He agreed soberly and looked at Eli. "Aren't you coming in?"

Eli shook his head. "I've got something to do."

"I'm going with you," Conley said quietly. "But let's stop at Brady's. I need something against the chill."

A half-dozen men were inside Brady's tavern. Conley stepped inside and said, "Eli and Lacey were burned out."

Faces showed shock, then rage. "Who did it?" several of them yelled.

Eli shook his head. "I'm not sure."

Kenmore peered at him, then asked shrewdly, "You think it was Haines?"

"He thinks it was Haines," Conley answered dryly.

"Let's ride out to his place," Kenmore said.

"He won't be there," Eli said shortly.

"No, but we can tell if he has been there. It's a starting point."

Eli considered it, then said, "Maybe you're right."

Every man in the room insisted upon going. Brady closed his place to go with them. But first he poured a round of drinks.

Eli sipped at his drink, looking at the savage, gleaming eyes. A moment before he had felt alone and friendless. The feeling was gone now.

He said, "I've got to unharness one of the team."

Kenmore said, "No. I've got a horse for you."

They rode out of Trading Post, and Eli looked at the hard, intent faces about him. He had forgotten to tell them one thing—if they found Haines, the man was his.

Haines's house was dark when they reached it. Eli heard the murmurs of disappointment rising about him and said, "I didn't think he'd be here."

He hailed the house and received no answer. The house had an empty, abandoned feeling, and Kenmore said, "If he was here, he's gone."

"I'll look inside," Eli said.

"See if you can find any tracks," Kenmore yelled.

Eli saw matches flare into life as he walked into the house. Somebody had gone through the house hurriedly. He saw bureau drawers opened, and looked at their pawed-through contents. It looked as though somebody had trouble in making up his mind what to take.

Haines, he thought bleakly. He made a quick dash in here for things he needed. How many hours start did he have? It didn't matter, for Eli's mind was already set.

He went outside, and Kenmore said, "He was here. I've shoed his mare enough to know that track anyplace."

Eli heard the muttered cursing, then Brady's voice raised savagely, "Burn his damned house."

His words were picked up and given roaring approval by the others.

"No," Eli said sharply.

They looked at him in astonishment, and Eli asked simply, "What good would that do?"

He mounted and his eyes rested on each man in turn. "I'm going after him."

"Hell, Eli," Kenmore exploded. "You can't track him at night. And by morning, you'll never catch up with him."

"I'll stop at every town, every house and ask. Somebody has to see him."

"That could take days," Kenmore protested.

More likely weeks, Eli thought. He said stubbornly, "I'm going."

Several of them insisted they were going with them. He said, "You can't. You've got womenfolk to think of. Judge," he asked, "can Lacey—"

"That's a fool question to ask," Conley interrupted brusquely. "You know she's welcome with us."

Kenmore sighed and asked, "You got plenty of ammunition, Eli?"

"Enough," Eli said.

He rode a little way, then looked back. They were gathered in a tight group, watching him. He lifted his hand in a salute, and every man responded.

CHAPTER SEVENTEEN

A month was behind Eli when he returned to Trading Post, a hard, demanding month, stamping its weary miles on both man and horse. He stopped the horse before Kenmore's blacksmith shop and stepped out of the saddle. He grunted at the small impact his heel made with the earth. His stiff and weary body protested the slightest jar. He rested his hand briefly on the animal's neck and said, "You'll get your rest now."

He walked into the shop, and for a moment the three men didn't see him. He asked, "Isn't anybody speaking to me any more?" and smiled wanly.

They whirled at the sound of his voice and stared at him wide-eyed. Kenmore was the first to reach him, and those powerful arms squeezed the breath out of him. Conley's hand rested on one shoulder, and Murphy's fist pounded Eli's left arm.

"My God, Eli," Kenmore said. "We'd just about given you up."

"Will you let go of me before you kill me?" Eli gasped.

Kenmore released his pressure and stepped back. He looked at Eli's haggard face, the drooping shoulders. He said quietly, "You've lost weight. You look like hell."

"I feel like it," Eli said with wry humor. "Did you think I'd stolen your horse?"

Conley said, "We were worried about you." He didn't ask about Haines. He didn't have to. The mark of failure was in Eli's eyes.

Eli said, "I never came in sight of him. Twice I thought I'd cut his trail. They were false leads. I think I rode every damned mile in southern Kansas." He was silent a moment, thinking about those miles. He had chopped wood for a dozen meals, and his rifle furnished the others. The sight of each house had brought its fresh hope, and the hope died as the house's occupants shook their heads. They hadn't seen a man of Haines's description.

"I rode through Fort Scott," he said. "Lots of federal troops there. I must have some kind of mark on me, the hard looks I got. I've been clear down to Oklahoma Territory, and I crossed the border and rode Missouri ground. People are pretty edgy. They didn't take kindly to a stranger asking questions."

"I'll bet he's still running," Kenmore said. "We'll never see him again."

Eli shook his head, but he didn't voice his disagreement. The odd conviction that some day he would run across Ross Haines again remained with him.

He asked, "What's been happening around here?"

"It's been quiet," Conley said. "But Jones went in with a big posse and sacked Lawrence. He got the town to turn over its weapons, then tore it apart. A fellow passing through here said Jones must have had two thousand men with him, a lot of them Missouri bordermen. They carried off everything they wanted."

"Where were Lane and Robinson?"

"According to this man, they ran. Walker surrendered the town."

Eli remembered the big, plodding man. After Lawrence's leaders ran, maybe Walker was left helpless. Maybe he couldn't do anything else.

He said, "That might explain something. In the past week I saw a dozen burned-out homes. I talked to some of the families. They claimed the raiders came from Missouri. It could be. They got away with it at Lawrence. Maybe it's spreading."

Kenmore said savagely, "They'd better leave us alone."

Eli said, "Words won't stop them. I think we'd better band together. If they hit us, we'll hit back hard and fast. Maybe we can discourage them."

He smiled faintly as he saw agreement on every face. "But

right now I'm only interested in getting something to eat. Then I'm going to sleep for a week."

Conley said, "Right now you're coming to the house. Lacey's been worried about you."

Eli hadn't forgotten about her. It was odd how many a night her face had appeared in a lonely campfire. But there had been no way to get in touch with her.

He asked, "Is she all right?"

"Fine," Conley assured him. "But come and see for yourself."

Conley stepped into the house first, and Eli heard him say, "Lacey, we've got a visitor."

Eli moved into the room, and Lacey's face went white at the sight of him. She tried to speak, and the words came out as a strangled, gasping sound. She rushed to him and threw her arms about him. "Eli, Eli," she said, and her voice was a little moan.

He held her close and was surprised at how glad he was to see her.

She stepped back, and her face was a rosy red. She said severely, "If you knew how we worried about you."

"I'm sorry for that, Lacey. But there was no way to let you know."

Her eyes ran over him. "You're so thin," she wailed.

He smiled faintly. "Meals were kinda irregular."

"I'd say you'd better feed him, child," Mrs. Conley said.

A look of understanding passed between them, and Lacey laughed. She turned and ran for the kitchen.

It seemed an eternity before the meal was ready. The savory odors floating from the kitchen made Eli's stomach rumble.

He sat down to a meal of fried eggs, bacon and potatoes. Lacey knew how to cook for a hungry man, for she set heaping platters on the table.

It was difficult to talk to her and eat at the same time, and he answered her eager questions with grunts. He finally said in exasperation, "Good Lord, Lacey, will you let me eat?"

He finished his meal and told her about the fruitless chase.

"I'm not sorry," she said defiantly. "It's over, Eli."

He thought a woman accepted things more readily than a man. He said flatly, "Not over, Lacey."

She frowned at him but changed what she had in mind to say. "What do you plan to do now, Eli?"

"After I sleep a week I thought I'd start rebuilding your house."

"I'd rather you'd start yours," she said.

That put a wave of color in her face, and he couldn't understand why. He stood and yawned. "We'll talk about it later. Now if I can borrow a bed from Judge Conley—"

He thought she would never leave the bedroom. "Lacey," he threatened, "if I have to I'll throw you out."

He was thinking about the long, lingering look she gave him from the door, when he fell asleep.

He fought the hand that was shaking him awake. It persisted, and he opened his eyes and looked at Kenmore. "Go away," he said. "I just got to sleep."

"You've slept fourteen hours," Kenmore grunted.

Some shadow in Kenmore's eyes drove the last of the sleep fog out of Eli's mind. He sat up and asked, "What is it?"

A hard, bitter shine was in Kenmore's eyes. "They didn't wait long to hit us. Julian and DeBeer were burned out last night. DeBeer was killed."

Some of that bitter shine was reflecting in Eli's eyes. "Did Julian recognize them?"

Kenmore shook his head. "But he says he has a funny feeling they were Missourians. Maybe by the way they talked. He thinks they came from some small town across the border with the idea of easy loot."

"Is he in town?"

Kenmore nodded. "His family is staying with Ben Murphy. We have Esther DeBeer and her children. DeBeer shouldn't have tried to resist them."

Not by himself, Eli thought. "I want to talk to Julian." He tugged on his boots and strode out of the room.

Lacey called to him as he went through the living room. He didn't even turn his head.

Julian had the resigned look of a man who has accepted the loss of everything he had. He described what had happened and said, "I think they came from one town. They seemed to know each other well. They treated it like a game."

"What did they take?" Eli asked.

"My wagon and team. My riding horse."

Eli knew the chestnut Julian rode, and he would recognize the team and wagon if he saw it. "What else?"

"All the household articles they could carry off. Mirandy begged them to leave clothing for the children and not to burn the house. They laughed at her."

"I suppose they took DeBeer's animals, too."

Julian nodded. "I guess they did."

A woman's sobbing came from Murphy's house.

"I ought to go to Mirandy," Julian said uncertainly.

Eli put his hand on Julian's shoulder. "Tell her not to worry too much."

His eyes held a vicious glow as he watched Julian walk into the house.

Kenmore said savagely, "I'll round up the men."

"What for?" Eli asked almost absently.

Kenmore looked baffled. "But you said if they hit us we'd hit back hard and quick."

"I still mean it. Who are we going to hit?"

"Goddam it, Eli," Kenmore said. "We can't just forget about it."

"I don't intend to," Eli said calmly. "I know Julian and DeBeer's horses. I'm going to cross the border and see if I can find them. If I can, we'll know who to hit."

"I'm going with you."

Eli shook his head. "A lone man can do better." He grinned bleakly at Kenmore. "Particularly if that man says he's a slavery man, run out of Kansas because of his beliefs."

Kenmore muttered, "Maybe you're right. I'll saddle another horse for you."

He came back in a few minutes, leading a bay. "He's fast," he said. "I put your rifle in the scabbard."

Eli pulled it out and handed it to him. He followed with his pistol.

"Are you crazy?" Kenmore demanded. "You can't ride over there unarmed."

"I want them to think I'm helpless." Eli mounted and looked at Kenmore. "I'll be back as soon as I can. Hold everybody ready. Tell Lacey I was called away on business."

It wasn't a lie. What happened to the community happened to him. Bromley had said it so long ago.

He thought his luck was going to be bad. He was riding through his fourth Missouri town late in the afternoon when he saw the horses in the corral outside of the blacksmith's shop. His eyes burned as he saw Julian's chestnut. He rode closer, and there was no mistaking it.

He wanted to race back to Trading Post and announce he had found the raiders. But Julian's chestnut being here wasn't positive proof. Smiths traded in horses—the man could have bought the animal from one of the raiders.

Direct questions would only arouse suspicion. Any knowledge he gained would have to come by a devious route. He picked the restaurant as the place to start. If it had been night he would have selected the saloon. A fat man with a huge belly was behind the counter. The creases in his round face said he laughed often.

"What'll it be, friend?"

Eli said wearily, "All I can afford is coffee."

The man asked, "You run into trouble?"

"They burned me out. Took everything I owned. I saved my horse by having him hid out."

The man's eyes turned wary. "Where did this happen?"

"Big Springs. In Kansas. The damned blue-bellies did it."

The wariness was fading. "You know it was blue-bellies?"

Eli nodded. "Some of them were my neighbors. I recognized

them. I'm getting out of that goddamed country. I'm going to settle down in Missouri where I can find some peace."

The fat man leaned over the counter. "I can tell you how to get something to replace the things you lost." He laughed at the skepticism in Eli's face. "You stay with us, and in a few night's time you'll get back everything you lost plus a little more."

Eli said, "I don't know what you mean."

The man took his apron off and came around the counter. "I'll show you. I'm Odie Doyle."

Eli took the meaty hand. "Eli Dryden." He followed the fat man out the door.

Doyle gave him a tour of the town. Eli saw the horses and wagon stolen at Trading Post. He even saw the highboy Mirandy was so proud of.

He said, "I don't understand."

Doyle laughed. "We took all this off the blue-bellies the other night. In a few raids a man can get rich. All the towns up and down the border are doing it."

Eli asked, "Who goes on these raids?"

"The town leaders. Anybody who wants to ride with us. And there's no danger. None of us got a scratch."

You will, Eli promised him silently.

He met the town's businessmen, and they laughed as they described the raid. Doyle laid an arm across Eli's shoulders and said, "He's going with us on the next one."

Eli drank with them that night, and when he protested he couldn't pay, it didn't matter. One raid would fill his pockets.

Doyle said, "You come sleep at my house until we ride again."

This was only a sport to Doyle and the others, a sport with little danger and much profit. A widow's tears couldn't reach this far.

Doyle asked, "Have you had enough?"

"Enough," Eli said. Doyle meant the whisky. Eli meant something entirely different.

He slipped out of Doyle's house in the middle of the night. He saddled and walked the horse out of town. He looked back at it, peacefully sleeping. It looked like an ordinary town intent only on the business of its living. It was a den of thieves. A lawyer had been on that raid, a restaurant owner and the man who owned the general store. All sharing dishonor with farmers, smiths and carpenters. All thinking they could grow wealthy by looting free-state men in Kansas. The town should treasure its peaceful hours. It didn't have a great many left.

Thirty armed men ringed a Missouri town. Dawn highlighted the savage hunger in their faces. It drove away the bulky shapelessness of the buildings and brought them into sharp relief. Somewhere across town, a rooster crowed. Julian was there and Kenmore and Murphy. Judge Conley's face showed a weariness after the hard night's ride.

The town was bottled, and the armed men were the cork. They kept glancing at Eli, impatience in their faces. He waited for the dawn to strengthen.

Across the street a door opened, and a man, his face heavy with sleep, stepped into the yard. He yawned and scratched himself. He turned his head and looked down Eli's rifle barrel. His face went gray with terror.

"Keep still if you want to live," Eli said.

There was no resistance in the man, and he seemed to have lost his voice. He stumbled ahead of Eli's rifle into the square.

As other men stepped out of their houses they were herded into the square. Each house was entered, forcefully if necessary, and the male occupant added to the growing number of prisoners. Kenmore came out of a house, pushing Doyle ahead of him. Doyle was in his nightshirt. He sputtered angry protests until he saw Eli. His mouth sagged, and the ruddy tinge in his face changed to a doughy white.

Eli asked, "Are you enjoying your sport now, Doyle?"

Doyle's body was a great mass of jelly.

Something warned Eli, and his eyes swept the houses. A man appeared suddenly in a second-story window, his rifle muzzle searching out a target. DeBeer had been this foolish, Eli thought as he fired.

The bullet's impact slammed the man backward. Eli heard a woman's scream, then the thin, frail sound of her crying. His face didn't soften. There had been a dead man in Kansas and a woman's crying, too.

"Take what you want," Eli ordered his men. He and a half-dozen others stayed with the prisoners. He could have guarded them by himself, for fear had put its weakening grip on them.

They looted the general store and seized tools from the smithy's shop. Confiscated wagons were loaded high, and saddleless horses were tied to tail gates.

"We'll burn the town," Brady yelled.

"No," Eli said. "Burn two houses." There was no way for an equal accounting in matters like this. One side or the other always got interest. If the interest fell to free-state men, it was more than time.

Eli looked at the huddled prisoners. "We could've burned the town. Step one foot into Kansas, and we'll come back."

Plumes of blackish smoke rose from two houses on the outskirts. The smoke swelled and joined, forming a cloud which hung over the town. The wind carried the sound of the crackling flames.

Eli moved out, and a column of horsemen and wagons fell in behind him. He looked back after a couple of hundred yards. The huddled prisoners were breaking and running. Not for weapons, he was certain—but to fight fire in the two houses in the hopes of saving the town.

Except for the burning houses, the town looked much the same as when Eli first saw it. But it was shattered spiritually. It had been a hard, object lesson. And if it didn't take, he was ready to administer another.

CHAPTER EIGHTEEN

Terror struck indiscriminately on both sides of the border. Men died defending their homes, and others ran, leaving the ruins of theirs. In Kansas three hundred families were burned out in one month. It was a rare night when an orange glow wasn't visible somewhere on the horizon. Men shivered and drew closer together. Only in numbers was there any safety at all.

On the Kansas side of the border Eli Dryden's name was spoken with respect. On the Missouri side it was always accompanied by curses. He could have had hundreds of men riding with him, but he kept the number small, wanting the mobility a smaller band brought. He rode almost nightly, and flesh melted from his frame. His face thinned until the eyes were the most prominent feature, and they seemed to be in constant, predatory questing.

In the lonely, retrospective hours conscience strode through his mind, kicking down the barriers he erected against it. It pointed out that innocent people were suffering along with the guilty, and he argued he couldn't help that. There wasn't time to check out every aggression and be certain who committed it. He couldn't sit futilely by because he couldn't pinpoint guilt. The Missourians raided into Kansas and looted and burned. He struck back at Missouri farms and Missouri towns in retaliation. This matter of retaliation was weighed on an insensitive scale. He could no longer point a finger at somebody and say, you're guilty. Now it could only be a lumping of pro-slavery men against free-state men. At this point he always cursed the small voice. If he was angry enough he could banish it—for a while.

He had no home any more, nor did he need one. He slept where the place and time were available, and he ate in the same manner. Until other men laid down their arms he would keep his handy.

He walked into Brady's, and Judge Conley was talking to Dan. Conley looked tired and frail.

Brady asked, "Are we riding again tonight?"

Eli nodded.

Conley said quietly, "Count me out tonight, Eli."

Brady's face was sympathetic. "Tired, Judge?"

"In every way. Where's it going to end, Eli?"

Eli frowned. Conley sounded like an accuser. He asked harshly, "Why this sudden change, Judge?"

Conley shook his head. "The law's always been the most important thing in my life, Eli. And yet I willingly broke it. Oh, I justified it like all of us. What is the real truth? Do I like being an avenger? Do I like bringing terror to other men?"

"Do you like lying down and letting them walk over you?"

"No. But what we're doing doesn't solve anything. We punish them, and they punish back. It keeps getting bigger and bigger instead of shrinking."

It was a valid argument, and Eli searched for an answer. Brady asked, "Judge, what got you to thinking this way?"

"The last raid. We burned out that little man and his family. The stuff he had wasn't worth carting away. He begged us to believe him when he said that all he wanted was to make a living. Does that sound familiar to you, Eli?"

"He was in Missouri," Eli said flatly.

"Is that enough for you any more? Eli, I think we've gone too far. I think we've forgotten what we set out to do."

Eli said quietly, "You don't have to ride with us again."

Conley's voice was equally low. "I don't intend to."

The door opened, and Thomas Moran came in. He was a likeable little Irishman, with a ready temper and equally ready laughter. He said, "You all set to do a little more jay-hawking tonight, Judge?"

Conley looked perplexed, and Moran laughed. "We've got a bird in Ireland that does all its hunting at night. It's called a jayhawk. I figure we've been doing a little jayhawking our-selves."

Conley smiled faintly. "Not tonight, Thomas. Good eve-ning, gentlemen."

Moran stared after him in open-mouthed astonishment. "What's wrong with him?"

Brady put an uneasy glance on Eli. "Nothing," he said shortly. "He's just tired."

Eli stared bleakly at the far wall. Had he ridden onto the wrong fork of the road without realizing it? Was he riding for excitement's sake and no other? Men listened to him and followed his orders. Did he like the power and authority? He argued against those points. Hadn't he made the country around Trading Post dangerous for the Missourians to enter? He was doing a needed job, and Conley had the gall to crit-icize it.

Brady said, "Let's have a drink and forget it."

He poured the whisky, and Eli stared moodily at his glass. If Conley was suggesting that Eli let the law handle it, he was wrong. If Conley could show him impartial law, he might listen to him. He clenched his hand around the glass. It had been a long time since that hand had held a farming imple-ment. He wondered if it ever would again.

He looked at Moran and said, "Conley's quitting. Does it bother you?"

Moran was quick and emphatic. "Hell, no. He's in his dotage."

Brady was slower in response. Conley was a friend of long standing. He said uneasily, "He's tired, Eli. He'll see it differ-ently tomorrow."

"No," Eli said. "I don't want him to see it differently."

He turned and strode out of the place. Let all of them wa-ver. He knew he never would. He would ride alone if necessary.

He made three raids the following week, and Conley's de-fection didn't seem to bother the others. When he passed Conley on the street, he spoke to him, and Conley always replied with courtesy. But there was a wide canyon between them, and both men knew it.

After the last raid he was sleeping in Kenmore's barn.

Kenmore shook him awake and said, "Somebody here to see you." He grinned at Eli's tenseness. "He's friendly."

Eli tugged on his boots. Lord God, he was tired. "Who is it?"

Kenmore shook his head and grinned mysteriously.

Eli stepped out of the barn, and a hand clamped on his shoulder. His first thought was that Kenmore had betrayed him. He whirled, knocking the hand from his shoulder, and was ready to spring, when Walker's grinning face came into focus.

He said, "Sam," and the tension drained from him. He made a mental apology to Kenmore.

Walker said, "You're drawn kinda fine, aren't you?"

"Not enough sleep," Eli grunted. He felt ashamed of his reflexes. But when a man hunted like an animal, he picked up an animal's instincts.

His eyes sharpened as he saw the badge pinned to Walker's vest. "What brings you down here?"

"I had some business down this way. I thought I'd drop by and say hello."

Eli's eyes were pinned to the U. S. marshal's badge. It made him feel sick. Walker had defected to the other side.

Walker said, "Look at the trees. It scares you to think that winter's so close."

Another cycle of leaves had matured, colored and were now dropping. Eli said, "You didn't come here to talk about the weather."

Walker said dryly, "You've been pretty busy."

"What have you heard about me?"

"The pro-slavery newspapers are calling you the scourge of the border."

Eli laughed.

Walker's face was grave. "It's no laughing matter. They're well aware of you, and they'll do their best to stamp you out."

Eli made an impatient gesture. He was in no mood to listen to a lecture. "What's been happening, Sam? We get no more than an occasional rumor."

"John Brown massacred five men on Pottawatomie Creek. Hacked them to death with swords. He's hurt our cause. People are shocked at what he did. They can become sickened by violence and turn against it."

By indirection he was referring to Eli Dryden, and Eli said heatedly, "None of the violence comes from them?"

Walker said patiently, "It does. Why this thing hasn't broken into open civil war I'll never know. But men on both sides are now trying to use reason instead of blind force."

"I've been using blind force?"

"Haven't you?" Walker asked quietly.

"I did what I was forced into."

"The excuse every man uses," Walker murmured.

Eli glared at him and turned to walk away.

Walker caught his arm. "Listen to me, Eli. I pinned on this badge because I thought I could do the most good this way. We've got a new governor. Geary's trying to bring law and order. Do you know a pro-slavery man was tried last week for murder of a free-state man? Tried and convicted by a jury of his own kind. Sam Jones has resigned, and Governor Geary refused to appoint another sheriff like him. Geary's convinced both sides are in the wrong. He's calling for a new election, and this time it'll be a lawful one."

"Are you trying to tell me to quit, Sam?"

"Yes. While there's time."

"Do you know what would happen if I did? All the border scum would rush in here. What would happen to my friends?"

"Whatever excuse you use, Eli, you're looting and killing. They're crimes. Don't make me ride down this way again."

Eli's eyes went cold. "Is that a threat, Sam?"

"Call it a warning, Eli."

"Don't ever come down here with a warrant for me, Sam. My people wouldn't let you get out alive."

There was a subtle hardening in Walker's face. "I hope I don't have to, Eli."

Eli had a final question. "Would you arrest Lane?"

"As quick as anyone else. I think he knows things are rolling past him. I'm afraid he'll do something desperate."

Eli laughed without mirth. "Jim Lane and John Brown. I'm not in very good company, am I?"

"No," Walker agreed. He mounted and looked down at Eli. "Think about what I said, Eli."

Eli nodded. The nod wasn't much of a promise.

He watched Walker ride out of town, then turned. Lacey stood watching him. That look of reproach was in her eyes again. It seemed to be there often any more, and it made him uncomfortable.

"Eli, was that a sheriff?" There was a breathless quality to her voice.

"No, a U. S. marshal."

She acted as though she dreaded to ask the question. "Was he after you?"

He said with quick impatience, "Good God, no. He's an old friend. He just stopped to say hello." His eyes bored into her. "What made you ask?"

She made a false start, then said helplessly, "Nothing, Eli."

He said harshly, "You don't think what I'm doing is right, either."

"I didn't say that," she said hotly.

They were close to another fight, and he said wearily, "Stop it, Lacey." He took her arm. "I'll walk you home."

"Home," she said bitterly. "I haven't any home. I'm living on the kindness of the Conleys."

She sounded as though everything was his fault, and he said defensively, "When have I had the time to even think about building?"

"You've forgotten a lot of things, Eli. You've even forgotten what you came to Kansas for."

His eyes grew cold. "We built once, and it was taken away from us. I'm only making sure it won't happen again."

"Is that the way you justify it, Eli?"

He didn't have to justify anything he did to her. He said, "It's none of your concern." They were in front of the Conley house, and he would be glad to get away from her.

Her eyes misted with tears. "None of my concern," she cried. "When I worry every minute what's happening to you? When I torture myself by thinking you might not come back?"

He stared into her eyes, seeing the longing and the need in them. A queer trembling started inside him, and he said hoarsely, "Lacey, are you saying—"

She said simply, "I've loved you from the moment Cass brought you home."

A man stumbled over answers right before his eyes. He said, "Lacey," and opened his arms. She came into them with a little sigh. It was the first time he had kissed her. He felt the quivering of her mouth under his. Her lips were young and inexperienced. Then the quivering was gone, replaced by a demand. A woman was like a flower; it took the touch of the right man to make her blossom.

He lifted his head, and he never had to look at the sky again to see stars. They were all in her eyes.

He shook his head, and she asked, "What is it?"

"I was just thinking of how long it took me to see you standing before me."

The old, mischievous glint was back in her eyes. "Maybe you're not very bright."

He laughed and pulled her close to him again. Neither of them saw Mrs. Conley come to the door, look out, then tiptoe softly away.

She asked, "Eli, when can we start building our home?"

He pushed her away, an instant suspicion in his eyes. "Was all this planned to get me to do what you want me to do?"

For a moment she was bewildered, then she said furiously, "I won't even answer that."

"Nothing's changed," he said evenly. "Until they stop, I can't stop."

"Maybe you won't ever be able to stop," she cried. She whirled and fled into the house.

He wanted to go after her, but he wouldn't let himself. A woman had to see what her man was up against. He felt heavy and defeated. And just a moment ago he could have raced up mountains and torn them apart with his bare hands. This was what happened when a man took his eyes from his main purpose.

He came up out of a sound sleep, and by the light of a lantern he saw a dozen anxious faces.

Kenmore said, "Eli, Proctor spotted fifty men camped in the woods about a mile from town."

Eli shook his head to clear it. "Who are they?"

"We don't know. I've sent out word to everybody."

Eli sat for a moment in thought. So they were getting bold enough to attack him in force. The last thing he wanted was a pitched battle in town.

He said, "We'll take the fight to them." This was the thing Lacey and Walker refused to understand. If he wanted to quit, those people against him wouldn't let him.

He waited while men slipped into town one or two at a time. Repetition made this night's summons familiar.

He set out with forty men, but surprise should offset the numerical odds.

Proctor threw up his hand after a short ride, and Eli saw the glow of campfires ahead. He shook his head. Surely, men stupid enough to build fires as carelessly as that didn't hope to catch a sleeping town.

They dismounted and tethered horses well out of earshot of stamping hoofs or the jingle and creaking of accouterments. Shadows flitted from tree to tree until the camp was surrounded. A bumbling man led this group, Eli thought. He hadn't even put out sentries to protect his sleeping camp.

Only one man seemed to be awake, a brooding, seated figure staring into a campfire. He rose and threw a log on the fire. By the increased light of the flames Eli recognized Jim Lane.

He called, "Jim. Jim Lane. It's Eli Dryden."

Lane jerked his head and peered into the blackness. Anxiety didn't leave his face until Eli stepped into the light.

"It's really you, Eli," he said, and pumped Eli's hand.

Eli couldn't return the enthusiasm. Around him men were waking, and in answer to their worried questions Lane called, "It's all right. A friend of mine."

Eli looked around the camp. Proctor had overestimated Lane's force. Eli put it closer to thirty men.

Lane chuckled. "They're understandably jumpy. Coffee, Eli?"

Eli shook his head. Once he had gratefully accepted coffee from this man.

He said, "A dozen men could have wiped out this camp. My God, Jim. Don't you put out sentries?"

Lane flushed and his mouth tightened.

Eli remembered how Lane reacted to criticism and didn't care. He asked bluntly, "What are you doing here, Jim?"

Lane's smile was a strained effort. "Waiting for daybreak. I didn't want to ride into your town in the darkness."

"You were wise," Eli said dryly.

"You've been doing great things, Eli. People are talking about you all over Kansas."

Lacey didn't think Eli was doing great things. Neither did Sam Walker. The thought irritated Eli. He could have readily turned that irritation against Lane, but the memory of a debt held his tongue.

Instead he asked, "How are things going for you, Jim?"

"Fine, fine," Lane said heartily. But a brooding in his eyes belied his words. He asked too casually, "Have you seen Sam Walker?"

"Yes." The single word was noncommittal.

"I had to drop him, Eli. He was a weak, frightened man."

Eli's face was impassive as he thought of Walker's slow, stolid strength.

"I could have saved Lawrence for them," Lane said. "But neither Robinson nor Walker would listen to me." He wore his most charming smile as he shrugged. "There was no use in me going down for a lost cause. If the slavers had captured me, Kansas would have been lost."

Eli stared fixedly at him. Did Lane believe that, or did he have to try to believe it to bolster his ego? Eli looked at a vain, selfish man, a man filled with thoughtless, bombastic words. But men would follow him until they became disillusioned. The saviors of Kansas wouldn't be the Jim Lanes. The realization hit Eli suddenly. No, the saviors would be more like Sam Walker, men who walked the middle of the road, rejecting the extremes at both edges. Where did Eli Dryden fit in this new reappraisement?

He thought stubbornly, I'm only doing a job that has to be done. Are you, an inner voice argued with him. Jim Lane is saying the same thing. Men follow him too. Eli's spirit recoiled at the comparison. The simple job he had set out to do had broadened and become complex. Trading Post was relatively safe, but he hadn't stopped. What did he really want? Not peace, the inner voice said. You've rejected that. Then it had to be power, the power to decide other men's thoughts and actions, the power that Jim Lane wanted. Had Lane started the same way and become so lost that he could no longer find his original road? It could happen to a man, Eli admitted.

Eli's silence didn't bother Lane. He said, "I knew when I first saw you, Eli, that you had that touch of greatness. Throw your men in with mine, and I'll make you a colonel. Do you know I've raised an army of men in Nebraska just waiting until I give the word?"

Eli said flatly, "And we'll sweep everybody before us who doesn't agree with us?"

"That's it," Lane said delightedly. "There's one fast, sure way to end this. We'll ride to Lecompton and kill every damned legislator the slavers elected. Won't that make the slaveholding bastards run?"

Lane was proposing a bloodbath so sweeping that it would

focus the nation's eyes on him. The army would have only one order—hunt down the perpetrators.

"You must be crazy," Eli said slowly.

Lane's face tightened. "What do you mean by that?"

"Even if you succeeded you couldn't run far enough to hide."

"Are you afraid?" Lane sneered.

The cords bunched in Eli's neck, but he said evenly, "You'd better take your men and ride out."

Lane's face darkened with anger. "And if I don't propose to?"

Eli said, "Listen." He called off names, and his men answered him. The voices came from every direction around the camp. "Then you'd be a fool."

Lane's face turned heavy with defeat. "Sam Walker turned against me. Now you. I could have made a great man out of you."

This was a pitiful man living with his illusions. But he could be dangerous, for he would strike out blindly trying to make those illusions come true.

"A word of warning, Jim. Sam's a U. S. marshal now. Don't do anything to make him come looking for you."

Lane cursed Walker with every oath at his command.

Eli's face grew colder. "Pack up and ride, Jim. We'll escort you out of the country."

The desire to curse Eli trembled on Lane's lips. He was wise enough to hold it. He turned and began saddling, the viciousness of his mood showing in the way he jerked the cinch strap tight.

Eli said, "Move out, Jim. And don't come back."

Lane said, "You'll regret this."

Eli sighed. He already did. He had a long night ride ahead of him, a ride with no practical purpose except to see that Lane got safely out of the country. He had a head filled with troubling thoughts, thoughts that would keep him awake long after this ride was finished. A man could easily raise followers by promising them violence, for that seemed to be a basic need of men. But when that need became satiated, what then? When men wanted to turn back to peace, where did the man who had incited them stand? Once half of Kansas would have listened to Jim Lane. Tonight he had thirty men, and tomorrow the number would be even less.

Eli's thoughts forced him toward a conclusion he didn't want to reach. The man who thundered and roared defiance was the shadow man. The one who coped with his emergency problems as best he could, only wanting to return to his normal living, was the solid man.

CHAPTER NINETEEN

The winter was long and brutally cold. Some families reported they burned as much as two cords of wood a week. It took all a man's time just chopping and sawing to keep warm. The winter's severity no doubt had a great deal to do with keeping the terror down. Over a month passed without a single report of a family being burned out reaching Eli. The inactivity palled on some of his men, and he saw how readily men could change from one kind of a life to another.

The strain between Lacey and himself continued. Oh, they talked politely enough, but they never said what was in their eyes. Mrs. Conley had disapproving eyes whenever she saw Eli, and he wondered what Lacey had told her.

He moved toward Kenmore's blacksmith shop, casting an eye at the sky. The sun would be out in full strength by this afternoon. It should further diminish the snow cover. They might even see a piece of bare ground by late afternoon, and it would be a welcome sight.

Kenmore's shop was a favorite loafing place. Eli found a half-dozen familiar faces crowded near the forge, absorbing its heat.

Kenmore said amiably, "You damned loafers get under-foot." He moved around one and thrust a glowing shoe into a tub of water.

Eli thought, Kenmore was the lucky one. There was always something to fill his hands and mind.

He stood there listening to the aimless talk until Tom Moran said, "I say we ought to move north. They're thick around Leavenworth. We've got this country pretty well tamed."

Eli heard words of agreement. He asked, "Tom, what did we set out to do?"

Moran looked puzzled. "Why we set out to run every damned pro-slaver out of Kansas."

Eli said, "We set out to make this part of Kansas safe for a man to build without fear of it being torn down."

Moran scowled. "You sound like—" He broke off and colored.

"Like Judge Conley?" Eli asked evenly. "Maybe our job is finished and we don't know it."

The voices were all in dissent. It hit him hard that these men didn't want to return to the monotonous tasks of ordinary living. Some of Walker's words came back—"a fast road and a dangerous one, and once a man's feet are firmly planted on it, it's hard for him to get off."

He said, "There's a new election next week. It could be an honest one."

"They'll steal it just like they did before," Moran shouted.

"You don't want things changed, do you, Tom? You want an excuse to go on like we are."

Moran flushed. "Are you saying I like this?"

"All of us do. We like riding into town and being heroes. But someday, the people will get tired of heroes. They'll want just plain, hard-working men who can build homes instead of destroying them." He saw disbelief on their faces. He surprised himself, for he had intended saying nothing like that.

"Have you gone soft?" Moran sneered. At the look in Eli's eyes he muttered, "Aw, Eli, you know I didn't mean that."

Eli nodded at the apology. "We will look for no more trouble. If it comes to us we'll take care of it." That had been his original intention, and somehow he had strayed from it. Maybe a man could step off that road, or at least slow down his pace.

He asked, "Is my horse outside?"

"In back, Eli," Kenmore said.

As Eli went out he heard the voices discussing what he had just said. They would take him apart and what they put back together might not be the man they had followed at all.

He mounted, and some vague, restless need riled him. He turned in the direction of his land. He passed the site of Lacey's house. The shed still stood, though it sagged toward the west. Dandy's bones were in it, and his face hardened. He had never repaid Haines for that.

He stopped where his house had stood. The pile of ashes had long since been blown or washed away. He stepped down, and a drumbeat began in his veins. When he started rebuilding, he would first have to cut new upright and supporting beams. The timber was still south of him, a lumber supply virtually untouched.

On this high prominence where the sun could reach it, the earth was bare. He reached down and took a pinch of it in his fingers. Its moistness left a stain. He stared unseeingly across the land, and the drumbeat strengthened. It was coming on planting time again. He had let a crop go unharvested and a planting pass by. Could he give up another as willingly?

Men had offered to help him rebuild once, and they would again if he asked. He thought of the look that would be in Lacey's eyes when he told her, and it was a reward he craved. He was suddenly eager to get back to Trading Post.

As he rode into town he saw Lacey coming out of Siegman's. That quick, little flash of light appeared in her eyes; it always did at sight of him. Then it seemed to dim as though she put an iron control over it.

He said, "Lacey, I've just been out to my place. I still think the original site is the best. But if you'd rather have it someplace else it's all right with me."

His words were fuel to that flash of light, strengthening it until a man was blinded by its brilliance.

"Oh Eli." She looked as though she wanted to laugh and cry at the same time. "Wherever you want to put it will be just fine with me."

He looked at her suspiciously. A docile, submissive Lacey. Who had ever heard of such a thing?

Ross Haines was in a vile mood. The winter had been long and confining, and he was sick of the poor accommodations in Fort Scott.

Doak Mueller sat across the table. He reached for the bottle and poured himself another drink. Haines stared at him with baleful eyes. He knew Mueller stayed around him because he kept him supplied with whisky. But a man had to have company.

Mueller was a big man with a heavy, slow face, but he had a cunning instinct about Haines's sensitive spots.

He said slyly, "It looks like you ain't ever going to run things. The way the election went, those free-staters got all the say-so now."

Haines's nostrils flared. The election returns were a stunning shock. District after district reported huge majorities for the free-staters. The governor had asked for federal troops to be stationed in fourteen districts where the Missourians were most likely to try to vote. This time, the border toughs were conspicuous by their absence.

Mueller grinned. "Yes sir, you're really hemmed in. You can't go home any more. I'll bet you wind up by losing your land."

"Shut up," Haines yelled, his face livid.

Mueller's eyes flickered. Maybe he had gone too far this time. Always before he had riled Haines, then listened to him rave with a sympathetic ear. It usually brought on a fresh bottle of whisky. But this time, Haines looked different. Mueller decided it might be wise to backtrack a little.

He said, "It's a damned shame, when a man can't return to his own land."

Haines rasped, "I'll kill that damned Dryden if it's the last thing I do." Dryden was solely responsible for keeping him in exile. The one time he had dared go back for needed clothing, he had seen Dryden and that Bromley woman driving into town. Even though he was a long way off he had almost panicked and run. Then the thought struck him. He could burn them out. That should make Dryden leave. Instead, it had sent Dryden after him, and Haines remembered his terror when he heard that Dryden was in Fort Scott looking for him. But Dryden hadn't asked the right people, or the ones who knew about him hadn't talked. Haines knew then he could never return home—not as long as Dryden lived.

Mueller said, "Why don't you bring this Dryden in? Every slave man in the territory would look up to you."

Haines sucked in his breath. How many times had he thought of that? But the doing was another matter. He couldn't possibly raise enough men who would dare venture into Dryden's country. He had pictured himself going in alone after Dryden. But that was all it was—a vague picture without substance.

"I'll get him," he said sullenly. His eyes dared Mueller to deny it.

The door opened, and Mueller said, "Here comes the lieutenant." He had an open contempt for army officers. They strutted big while they were in town, but the strutting disappeared whenever they were away from its safety.

He called, "Over here, Lieutenant." He waved a big hand at an empty chair. "We were just talking about Eli Dryden."

Welles Barnes pulled out the chair and sat down. He was a thin-faced man with intense eyes set above high cheekbones. He wore a small mustache, and he had the abstract habit of stroking it.

"That coward," he said contemptuously. "I wish I could come to grips with him. All I've ever seen of him is his heels."

Mueller laughed. "Lieutenant, if he had any reason he'd come down here and wipe your town off the map."

Barnes's face burned. He said stiffly, "I wish just once I could meet him face to face."

"Bringing him in would kinda shine up your name, wouldn't it, Lieutenant?" Mueller asked softly. "It might even get you a promotion. But I never heard of a promotion doing a dead man any good."

Barnes's eyes blazed. He had never been able to understand why a gentleman like Ross Haines tolerated such riffraff.

"That's enough, Doak," Haines said. But Mueller's words had planted a seed in his mind. Barnes was Southern born, sent on garrison duty from a plush Washington job. He hated the free-soil men, both from instinct and training and particularly because he blamed them for his being here.

Haines said, "Welles, why don't you take a company of dragoons and get this Dryden? It wouldn't hurt an officer's career."

Barnes said sullenly, "Because a lieutenant doesn't make his own orders." But Haines was right. The man who stopped Dryden's depredations would get headlines all over the country. He had asked the colonel to let him go after Dryden, and his cheeks still burned at the memory of the colonel's dressing-down. The army stayed out of politics, unless ordered otherwise by Washington. If Lieutenant Barnes had personal glory-seeking on his mind, he'd better rid himself of it.

Haines lowered his voice. "All right. You can't go after him. But what if he rode right into Fort Scott?"

Barnes thought about it. He could see himself capturing or killing the man. It was a pleasant dream, but it wasn't reality.

He said, "He wouldn't dare. Thanks for the drink, Ross." He stood and moved toward the door.

Mueller took no offense at Barnes's pointed ignoring. He chuckled and said, "You laid some tempting bait before him."

Haines said, "He made it plain enough he can't go after Dryden. But what if Dryden came down here?"

Mueller's eyes were shrewd. "Dryden don't want to tangle with the army."

"But he might come clear to the fort's walls after stolen horses. If Barnes was out on patrol and ran across him accidentally—"

Mueller said thoughtfully, "You might be able to put it together. Dryden sure as hell would come after stolen horses. Who's going to steal those horses?"

"I thought you might pick up some men and go after them."

"Not me," Mueller said emphatically. "I like my hide whole."

"Two hundred dollars for you and a hundred dollars for every man who goes with you. Plus any horses you can steal."

Mueller puffed out his breath. Two hundred dollars was a lot of money. It ought to patch quite a few holes in his hide. He pointed a finger at Haines. "On one condition. That you go with us. You know the country."

Haines held the flat refusal he wanted to make. Mueller wouldn't go otherwise. It was in his face. Haines shivered at the risk, but the gain could be worth it. With Dryden gone he could go home; he could reclaim his land. But most important of all, he could erase the blot on his honor.

His shakiness showed in his voice. "Pick three good men." A small band was less likely to be seen. If they did all their riding at night the risks would be minimized. Minimized but not eliminated. He swore at the sticky clinging of the thought.

He said, "Get men with the fastest horses you can find. Get—"

Mueller grinned. "I know what to get. Hell, I'm as scared as you are."

CHAPTER TWENTY

Two dozen mounted men assembled in the street of Trading Post. Eli asked, "What's the final count?"

Kenmore said, "They stole a dozen horses. Looks like five men did it. Their tracks head south."

The first report came in shortly after daybreak. Snyder reported two horses gone, Mulhill came in with a loss of three, and the others lost single animals. This raid had been stealthy and sly with no attempt made to awaken or harm the occupants of the farmhouses. In fact, it was just the opposite. Several men said they were awakened by their barking dogs, and they had suffered no losses.

A few men had made a quick run into his country and grabbed a handful of horses. If Eli caught them they would pay quite a price; they would pay with their necks.

Tracing them was going to be a simple matter. The bare earth was moist, taking a clear imprint. That southerly direction was a ruse. After a few miles the tracks would turn east and cross the border into Missouri.

He asked, "Ready?" and saw bobbing heads. Eagerness was in every face. This was activity after weeks of boring idleness.

He waved his arm forward, and the horsemen clattered after him.

They picked up the tracks at Snyder's place. Kenmore was right in his estimate of the number of thieves. Five men, each leading two or three horses. Those horses would slow them.

An hour went by, and Eli's frown grew. The tracks showed no indication of veering toward the border. And the raiders were making better time than he thought possible.

They stopped for a brief rest, and Kenmore said, "It looks like we'll have to run them clear to Fort Scott."

Eli shook his head. They wouldn't go that far. He had

avoided any direct conflict with the federal government, knowing its capacity for reprisal. If the stolen horses were in Fort Scott, two dozen men couldn't run its garrison out and recover the horses.

He said, "Let's move."

It was late afternoon when he caught the glint of a reflected sunray. He threw up his hand, halting the men behind him.

Kenmore asked, "What is it?"

"I saw a flash down there." Eli pointed toward a gulley, some five hundred yards ahead. "It looked like the sun hit metal."

His eyes swept what he could see of the gulley. It ran in the clear for a while, then ducked into woods on both ends. It was an excellent spot for an ambush.

He sat motionless for five minutes and saw nothing else. Around him men grumbled their impatience.

"It's clear," Kenmore said.

Eli gave him a sharp "No." His feeling told him that this was all wrong. He had learned to depend on that feeling.

"Tie the horses in the woods," he ordered. "And take cover."

None of the faces were happy about this new turn. They were losing too much valuable time. If Eli kept this up, they would never catch the thieves.

The earth's dampness soaked through Eli's pants and laid its cold touch on his skin. He heard men swearing, and it didn't change his mind. That stubbornness had served him well before.

They had the advantage of high ground. If men were concealed in that gulley, impatience must be working on them, too. That impatience would either drive them off or send them sweeping up the slope.

Moran's voice shook with excitement. "I saw something move down there. By God, look at them come out of the timber."

Eli had caught that first movement. He saw the flash of

drawn sabers and the blue of the uniforms. He judged there were thirty men charging up the slope. The odds weren't bad. But this was that direct clash with the army. Could they make a dash for their horses, mount and still have time to escape? He didn't think they could. The dragoons would be on them, cutting and slashing.

Tight faces turned toward him, and he said calmly, "Let them get closer."

Grins broke out up and down the line. They'd teach the army a little healthy respect.

Eli crouched behind his boulder and waited. The young officer leading the charge was well out in front and getting close enough for Eli to make out his features. The young officer was a fool. He was trying to take a superior position without knowing how many men were against him.

He aimed and fired a shot over the officer's head. Even that warning didn't deter him. He looked at his men and said, "Drop a few horses. I don't want a single man of them touched."

He thought that was rebellion on Moran's face, and said savagely, "I mean it, Tom. Those are U. S. troops."

Moran grinned sheepishly. "What if that doesn't turn them?"

"It will," Eli said.

He watched a jutting rock down the slope. When the officer reached the rock, Eli was going to cut the horse from under him.

He said "Now," and fired. A ragged volley broke out up and down the line. The officer's horse plunged to its knees, and Eli saw the man kick his feet clear of the stirrups. He went over his mount's head in a long roll, then was up on his feet and running. He had lost his sword and hat, and he seemed dazed.

The scene on the slope turned into disorder and confusion. Two of the downed animals regained their feet and raced into the mounted troops, breaking up their ragged line and creating more confusion. Dismounted men ran toward their mounted comrades, their upheld hands begging to be picked up. Eli saw a trooper swing toward the officer, a hand reached down, and helped swing the officer up behind him. Then the entire patrol wheeled about as though by common signal and fled down the hill.

Two dead horses lay on the field. Another struggled to get to its feet, and its front hoofs slashed the earth. Its hindquarters seemed anchored to the ground. Its shrill, agonized scream sounded like a woman in pain. Gut shot probably, Eli thought. He would have to shoot the animal again before he left.

Moran said with sour humor, "It didn't take much to fill their bellies."

Eli stared in the direction the fleeing men had taken. "Probably their first taste of fire," he said absently. "Did I see a civilian riding with them?"

He saw shaking heads. No one else had seen the man, and he decided that he had imagined things in the heat of the battle.

The wounded horse screamed again, and Eli said, "I've got to shoot him." He walked down the slope, and a half-dozen of his men followed him.

The horse still threshed about, though its movements were weaker. Eli saw the hole in its belly and smelled the raw, pungent odor of blood-drenched manure. He shot the animal through the head.

He turned, and Moran was stooping to pick up a discarded rifle. "Drop it," he ordered.

"Hell," Moran said indignantly. "It's a brand-new rifle."

"And it belongs to the army. Our army."

Moran let the rifle fall to the ground. "I guess I forgot, Eli."

Kenmore asked, "Are we going on?"

Eli shook his head. Fort Scott would be a stirred-up hornet's nest when that patrol made its report. The entire gar-

rison would be ready to storm out after them. He only hoped
they wouldn't follow them clear back to Trading Post.

He said, "We are not."

Snyder wailed, "What about my horses."

Eli bared his teeth in a humorless grin. "Washington will
be asking us the same question."

He kept glancing behind him as he walked back up the
slope.

No amount of whisky could still the shaking in Haines. The
afternoon's scene was vivid in his mind, and he relived every
moment of it. He had expected Dryden to break and run at
the first sight of the charge. And instead, Dryden had broken
and routed it. Haines could have cried at the waste of his planning—not to mention the risks he had taken. He had lured
Dryden straight into Barnes's hands, then the headstrong
young fool had fumbled it. Haines had advised waiting. But
Barnes had been fired up with the thought of how close he
was to Dryden, and the waiting had become unbearable.

He drank another shot of whisky and cursed Welles Barnes
and his driving ambition.

He lifted his head as the door opened. He called, "Colonel,
have a drink with me." He signaled the bartender to bring
another glass.

Colonel Belmont hesitated, then strode toward Haines's
table. He was a stern-faced man with a carefully trimmed
iron-gray mustache and cold eyes. Because of his position
Haines was acceptable at the post's social functions, and he
couldn't recall the colonel smiling. The man did everything by
the book, and he was a martinet about it. Some smolder-
ing rage was in Belmont's eyes as he sat down.

Haines poured, then said sympathetically, "A bad business."

Belmont glared at him. "I suppose it's all over town by
now. How the army was whipped by a handful of farmers.
The scum we get in the army now. Not a one of them with
guts enough to face an angry tomcat."

"Who was responsible?" Haines asked. He expected the

colonel to name Eli Dryden. By tomorrow morning Belmont would have the entire garrison in the saddle after him.

"I've talked to every man involved," Belmont said grimly. "Most of them didn't stay around long enough to see, and the others don't know."

Haines wanted to cry out, "It was Dryden. Eli Dryden." But he dared not involve himself in this. Evidently no one had reported him going with the patrol.

He licked dry lips. "Do you have any idea who it was?"

"I think it was Dryden," Belmont snapped. "I've been out to the scene. He picked a masterful place to wait for Barnes's charge. The man really responsible for our beating is Barnes. Charging up that hill against entrenched men." His frown deepened. "If it was Dryden, what pulled him so far south? He's been careful to avoid this area. And Barnes was north of his ordered patrol. It was almost like their meeting was planned."

Those cold eyes stabbed into Haines, and he quaked inwardly. Did the colonel know who had planned this? Haines had no idea of what the army's punishment would be, but he was certain it would be swift and terrible. He had to keep Belmont's attention on the main issue, and he asked, "Are you going after him?"

"You mean Dryden? He only defended himself. He could have wiped out the entire patrol. I've confined Lieutenant Barnes to his quarters, and I've sent a report to Washington, with a duplicate copy going to the governor. That's all I'll do until I get further orders."

Haines wanted to cry out in dismay. He said, "It's unfortunate Dryden can humilate the army and get away with it."

He had touched a sore, sensitive spot, for he had never seen such wild fury on a man's face.

"If he came down here once he'll come again," Belmont said savagely. "I pray God he'll ride into my territory again. I won't have to wait for orders then."

He repaired the cracks in the iron façade of his face and stood. "Thanks for the drink, Haines."

Haines watched him walk out of the door. He felt limp, and his face was damp. The disappointment made him sick. He wished Belmont had been leading that patrol. He wouldn't have made the mistake that young fool had made.

Haines poured another shot. An idea was forming in his mind. He had lured Dryden once; he had lured him almost all the way here. Why couldn't he do it again? His stomach churned at the thought of the risks involved. It would have to be a much more drastic plan. It had to be strong enough to make Dryden throw all caution aside, to enrage him so much that he would storm Fort Scott, if necessary. Haines's eyes were beginning to blaze as he thought about it. He had gone into Dryden's country and come out untouched. A careful, clever man could do it again. And money would buy him all the help he needed.

CHAPTER TWENTY-ONE

For a week Eli had men watching all the approaches to Trading Post. But the army's expected pursuit didn't come. He could reach only one conclusion. The army wasn't positive he was the man it wanted. He and Lacey had stormy words about it. She pointed out that he hadn't recovered the horses, that the whole incident had been useless. "What if the army does come?" she asked. "Will you stand and fight them?"

He remembered how angry he had been. She knew he couldn't fight the army. He and his men would have to slip away, to run. She had put his thought into words. "You'll have to run. And then you'll spend the rest of your life running."

He had said through clenched teeth, "Lacey—" Then he stopped.

Tears misted her eyes. "Eli," she wailed, and ran into his arms. "I tell myself that I'll keep my mouth shut. Then I hear myself talking again. Oh, Eli, I don't mean to be critical of you." She cried hard, her face muffled against his chest.

He stroked her hair and said, "It's all right."

Her voice was almost inaudible. "I want you with me."

He put a forefinger under her chin and lifted her face. "That's where I want to be." He kissed the tear-streaked cheeks, then the lips. "I don't think the army's coming, Lacey. I'm going out today and work on the house."

She clutched him and said, "I'll never interfere again. I'll go along with whatever you have to do and never say a word." She asked indignantly, "What are you grinning at?" Her lips trembled, then she broke into laughter. "Well, not many words, anyway."

She stood there, watching him as he rode away. He answered the lift of her arm with a wave. The hope that had shone in her eyes was in him. Maybe the time was nearing when a man could go about his own pursuits without fear of being attacked, or having to do the attacking himself. But he would keep the sentries out a while longer, for the army was slow to move.

His heart was light as he worked. This house was for Lacey, and he took special care in the building of it. Alicia had never been more than a dream, a dream with no substance. He could think of her now only with a rueful understanding. He had been young and callow. Alicia had been sweet and soft and wrapped in the allure of women. Beyond that, there was no depth to her. Beside Lacey, she was only a formless shadow.

He found himself whistling as he worked, and the discovery amazed him. How many months had it been since he had felt like whistling?

His whistling broke off abruptly, and he put down his hammer. He had the feeling he was under surveillance, and he scanned the surrounding country. He saw no movement, nor anything strange. The feeling slowly faded. The desire to whistle was gone when he resumed work. He supposed the feeling was a reaction to all the tense, keyed-up nights.

Haines and eight men lay on a hill outside Trading Post. It had taken two night rides to reach it, for Haines would not move in daylight. He lay on his belly, glasses trained on the town.

Mueller lay beside him, and he asked, "How long are we going to stay here?" He was nervous, and so were the other men. He could hear it in their soft swearing. This had cost Haines a lot of money, for he had given each man two hundred dollars. Haines had said he wanted to capture some of his old enemies. Mueller had demurred, thinking he meant Dryden. "Not Dryden," Haines had assured him. He had something else in mind for Dryden. He wanted to pull Dryden into Fort Scott and see him and all who rode with him destroyed.

Haines said passionately, "Goddam him. I've watched him for a week. He rides out to work on his house every day. Why isn't he going this morning?" He kept the glasses glued to his eyes.

He sighed with relief as he saw Dryden come around a building, leading a horse. Four men joined him. They mounted and rode in the direction of Dryden's land.

Haines waited until long after the horsemen were out of sight. He wanted to be certain Dryden wasn't returning for any small reason.

He stood and said, "Let's go. Pick up as many men as we can find. Let the women alone." He saw no disagreement on the faces. All they wanted was to get out of the town as quickly as possible. Half of their two hundred dollars was waiting when they returned to Fort Scott. The waiting money and fear of Dryden were all the prod they needed.

It was a lightning-quick strike. They rounded up four men in Brady's tavern and shoved them out into the street. Haines looked at Brady and said, "Bring him along, too."

He remembered all the times Brady had looked at him with spit in his eyes.

They collected nine men, and Haines didn't dare take time to search for more. Women were staring out of windows with white, frightened faces. At any moment, one of them could become bold enough to blast at them with a shotgun.

Judge Conley was among the nine men, and he stared unblinkingly at Haines. "Ross," he said, "you're a dead man for this."

Haines raised his quirt. He wanted to cut Conley to pieces. He restrained his temper. "You've got it wrong, Judge. You're the dead man."

They rounded up horses for the nine men and forced them to mount. They herded them south out of town, and Haines pushed them as hard as he could. He was soaked with sweat, and he didn't draw an easy breath until the timber closed around them.

Mueller asked, "What are you going to do with them?"

"You'll see," Haines replied curtly.

Mueller's eyes had an odd look. "You sure marked yourself with Dryden. A dozen people will be waiting to tell him when he comes back."

"None of these nine will."

Mueller's eyes were startled, and Haines asked coldly, "Does it bother you?"

Mueller thought of the money waiting for him in Fort Scott. "Not me," he said almost cheerfully.

They didn't ride too far. Haines wanted Dryden to find these men. He wanted him to know who did it. And he wanted him to know where he could find that man. All those things would send Dryden galloping clear through Fort Scott.

He herded the men into a gulch near the Marais des Cygnes River. He lined them up against the far embankment. He could see the raw nerves twitching in their faces, and the tongues licking at dry lips.

For the first time, his men realized what he intended doing, and one of them, near Haines, pulled his horse back.

Haines yelled, "Brockett, goddam you, wheel back into line."

"You intend killing these men," Brockett accused.

"I do."

"I'll have nothing to do with any such goddamed piece of business as this," Brockett said.

"You won't get your money," Haines roared.

Brockett didn't care about the money. He spun his horse and sank his spurs deep.

"Any of the rest of you want to give up your money, besides what they're carrying in their pockets and their horses?" Haines saw no more dissent, and he pulled his revolver and fired at Conley. Conley was flattened against the embankment. Shock twisted his features as he slid limply to the gulley floor.

A volley of shots followed, and the lined-up men fell to the ground. Thinking about the deed might have been hard, the doing of it wasn't difficult at all.

Men threw off and raced toward the fallen men. They had the bodies half searched before Haines reached them. One of them said, "This one's still alive."

"Let him be," Haines ordered. He wanted someone alive to tell Dryden about this.

He toed Conley over, and Conley still lived. He breathed hard, and each breath spewed reddened flecks. But his eyes were calm.

He whispered, "Ross, you've just committed suicide."

Haines kicked him in the face. "Tell Dryden he can find me in Fort Scott. If he's got the nerve to come after me."

Conley might not live to repeat the message, but Brady had only a shoulder wound. Haines was certain he would be alive.

He heard quarreling over the division of what was found in the pockets, and he yelled, "You can stay here all day arguing about pocket change. You can stay until Dryden gets here."

His words jarred them back to their senses. They were mounted almost as soon as he was.

CHAPTER TWENTY-TWO

A rider had been dispatched to tell Eli the news. Now he sat his horse in the middle of the street, waiting for the others to gather. Precious time was passing, and he forced himself to a semblance of calmness.

Kenmore came up and said, "They went south, Eli."

Eli nodded, his face wooden. A dozen people had told him that Haines led the band. Was Haines behind the horse-stealing raid? It was possible, though no longer important now. Nine of his men were missing, and Eli feared for their lives.

Kenmore asked impatiently, "How long are we going to wait?"

A dozen men had the same impatience. Every minute wasted here was a minute added to Haines's lead.

"Until the others get here," Eli answered. The daring of Haines's raid was a warning to go cautiously. Until Eli knew the reason behind Haines's insane action, he would let no emotion stampede him into doing what Haines wanted.

His face was blank as he thought about it. How far was he prepared to run Haines? Just as far as necessary, he thought bleakly. Into Fort Scott, right under the army's nose? He evaded a direct answer. He would face it when the moment arrived.

He looked across the street and saw Lacey standing in a doorway. He had expected a great deal more trouble from her. But she had looked at him dry-eyed and whispered, "Will it ever end, Eli?"

That was another unanswered question. But she hadn't

questioned the need of his going, and she hadn't tried to weaken him with tears and arguments. But he wished she would leave that doorway.

Mounted men trickled into Trading Post by twos and threes until the street was packed. Eli made a quick count. He had better than forty men. The band was large enough to have striking force and not too large to lose mobility. He stood in his stirrups and swept his arm forward. He didn't look at Lacey as he rode out of town.

They could have galloped and still not lost the tracks. Eli felt the fretting impatience of the men pushing at him, but he would not hurry. Had they forgotten the ambush of not too many days ago? They could be riding into another one. His eyes searched every patch of woods, every crest of the hills.

Kenmore said, "He'll have time to get them clear out of the country."

Eli gave him a savage glance. "If they're still alive."

Kenmore looked startled, and Eli asked, "What reason did he have to take them with him?"

"Ransom?" Kenmore hazarded.

"How much money could we raise among us?" He saw the distress on Kenmore's face and went on, "He might have taken them to bargain for something. But until we know, we're not adding any names to the list he already has."

Kenmore dropped back, pausing for a moment beside different horses. After a few minutes Eli no longer felt the impatience pressing at him.

He saw the heavy strip of woods along the Marais des Cygnes. If he were setting an ambush it would be on the other side of the river. Swimming horses were slow-moving, and their riders would be helpless targets.

A gulley lay just ahead of them, and that, too, was a logical spot. But his choice would have been the river.

He waved Kenmore up beside him and said, "We'd better take a look at the gulley."

Kenmore nodded, and they moved slowly forward. The

road crossed the gulley at its shallowest part. Eli could feel the strain of the unknown tightening him. He thought he heard a sound to his right and whipped his head that way. He saw the crumpled forms and said, "We've found them."

He heard Kenmore's savage cursing as he threw off and ran toward the still forms. His first impression was that they were all dead, then Dan Brady said in a weak voice, "I figured you'd be coming."

He had tried to fashion an awkward bandage about his blood-stained shoulder. "I'm all right," he said as Eli bent over him. "The judge is in bad shape. The others are dead."

Eli hurried to where Conley lay. Conley's eyes were closed, and Eli was sure he hadn't made it.

Then Conley's eyes opened, and the fading spark in them picked up a momentary strength. His face was badly bruised, and his nose looked broken. "I tried to hang on, Eli," he whispered. "It was Haines. He kicked me in the face after he shot me." He sounded as though the kick was the harder to bear.

Eli started to put an arm under Conley's head, and Conley said, "No use, Eli." That spark in his eyes was a fire now. "He lined us up and shot us down like dogs. For no reason. Except I think he wants you to follow him into Fort Scott. Eli, watch yourself."

Conley's fingers bit into Eli's hand at some new intensity of pain. He said, "I'm sorry, Eli. I think you were right, and I was wrong." The words took the last puff of breath. He died easily and with dignity. He merely closed his eyes.

Eli stood and looked at the faces around him. "Haines wants to draw us into Fort Scott. The army's garrisoned there."

Indignant voices arose at the suggestion that it might not be wisest to go on.

Eli nodded. "I thought you'd feel that way. Murphy, you and Moran take Dan to town. Then come back with wagons."

Moran started to protest, and Brady said, "I know how you feel, Tom. I wish I could be going on with them."

Moran's face changed instantly. "Don't you be fretting, Dan. We'll get you back." He glared about him. "Help him up with me." He slipped back from the saddle and onto the horse's rump.

They helped Brady into the saddle, and Moran's arms supported him. He said, "Eli, get in a lick for me."

Eli nodded. He had a lot of licks to get in.

The Marmaton River lay before them. They couldn't see it because of the night, but the lights of Fort Scott were just south of it. A stiff south wind blew into Eli's face, carrying sounds with it. He heard the baying of a hound from the woods, edging the river. Some coon hunter was running his dogs. That was one of the small dangers that haunted him. Someone like that hunter could spot them and make a hurried run into town. He shifted restlessly, and last winter's dried, thick prairie grass crackled under foot. The new green hadn't yet had time to take over and blanket the old. He heard the faint, sad, sweet notes of a bugle blowing taps. The army was going to bed.

He discarded one thought after another. He thought of going in alone and eliminated that. One man couldn't do much of a job of searching. A half-dozen could do a much more intensive job, but the chances of discovery would be multiplied by just that much.

He heard the rasp of a match and saw the flare of light as Julian lit a cigarette.

"Goddam it," he said. "Put out that match."

Julian said sheepishly, "I wasn't thinking, Eli." He blew out the match and tossed it into the grass.

Eli followed the tiny spark of its descent. That match wasn't dead. He sprang to the ground, and by the time he reached the spot, the spark had grown to a tiny flame licking hungrily at the dried grass. The stiff wind fanned it into avid, racing fingers of fire, and Eli spent several busy seconds, stomping it out.

He didn't rebuke Julian. Julian had handed him the answer of how to draw the people out of Fort Scott.

He asked, "Kenmore, if the people over there had to fight fire to save their town, would Haines join them?"

"Him?" Kenmore said contemptuously. "I never saw him do a lick of work or soil his hands. What are you thinking about?"

"If the prairie south of town caught fire, how many men do you think would leave Fort Scott to fight it?"

"Every able man. Except Haines. And that includes the army." Kenmore's eyes glowed. "A fire might give a man a chance to look for Haines."

"That occurred to me," Eli said.

They gathered around him while he explained what he had in mind. They would cross the Marmaton in two bunches. One bunch would take a circuitous route around the town and fire the grass some three miles south of it. They were to fire a long line, then withdraw and recross the river. Eli selected four men to go in with him. At the murmurs of disappointment around him, he said, "The rest of you move to the outskirts of town and wait. You may have to come in and get us out."

They approved of that, for the murmurs died.

They crossed the river together, and the water was cold above a man's boots. The splashing sounded distressingly loud.

The men who were to fire the grass moved off into the darkness, and for the others, the waiting and strain started.

A dozen times somebody asked, "Shouldn't they be there by now? Shouldn't we be seeing or hearing something?"

Eli said, "Not yet." It would take time for those men to swing around the town, additional time to ride south of it. In his mind's eye Eli could see them ready to set the fire. They each would gather a bunch of long, dried grass, light it, then run along a line, dribbling the flaming grass behind. Little spots of fire would start and spread slowly until they were devoured by others. A fire's appetite was insatiable. First it stood stationary, strengthening itself until it was strong enough to crawl. The crawl quickened to a rapid walk, then it was galloping as fast as a man could ride.

He had seen prairie fires, and they were terrible things. Flames roared higher than a man's head, whipping in fantastic whirls and curlicues, depending upon the caprices of the wind. The wild things fled before the flames, and the quick saved themselves. The others perished.

Eli said, "Climb a tree, Julian, and see if you can spot anything."

Julian picked a hackberry tree that grew straight and tall.

Eli waited until Julian became a formless, dark blur near the top of the tree. "See anything?" he asked.

"Nothing," Julian grunted.

Each passing minute was another brick added to an already crushing burden. There was no use calling to Julian again. Julian would tell them when he saw anything.

"Eli," Julian called. "I think I see fire beyond the town." He was silent, and Eli waited tensely.

"They got her started," Julian called. "She's beginning to roll. They see it in town, too. Listen."

Eli heard a bugle blaring and the tolling of a bell. Men would be rushing out into the streets and staring fearfully toward the south. In the fort, noncoms would be kicking sleepy men out of their bunks. In a few minutes men and horses would be racing toward the approaching terror. Wagons would follow, loaded with shovels, brooms and sacks—anything that would give a pair of hands something to beat at those flames.

Eli couldn't see the fire itself, but he could see the reflected orange glow of it in the sky.

"Come on down, Julian," he called.

He picked Kenmore, Murphy and three others to go in with him. These were the men who knew Judge Conley best.

He said, "Let's go." It would have to be a hard and rapid search, for their time margin wouldn't be large. They would need daring and a lot more luck. Eli prayed for that luck.

He stopped at the edge of town. Dark shadows grouped behind him. Five men detached themselves from the bulk of the shadow.

He said, "Look in the taverns, first. Question somebody if you have to. But find him. And don't try to take him out."

They knew what he meant, and they nodded agreement.

Eli looked down the street. It looked empty. The lights from the buildings washed across the street and bathed the tie-racks. They were as empty as the street. He still couldn't see the fire, but the glow in the sky was brighter. They would be backfiring out there, trying to destroy the fire by making it feed on itself.

He asked, "Ready?" and received positive nods.

Haines came out of the empty tavern. At the first alarm every man in the place had rushed out into the street, then scattered to get horses and tools. It was a wild, disorganized scene but still it had a sort of teamwork to it, for every man knew that the peril to others was a peril to himself.

Haines swore and turned back into the tavern. Even the owner had gone, not taking time to remove his apron. Haines poured himself a drink. The whisky had little power to smother the apprehension in him.

He downed the drink and reeled. The whisky was affecting his muscles but not his mind. His mind remained bell-clear. His face contorted as he thought of Belmont. Belmont was a colonel, and a goddamed colonel didn't listen to a civilian.

He had tried to stop Belmont from taking the entire garrison. He had tried to tell him that this was the night Dryden might attack.

"Let go of my bridle," Belmont had roared, and struck at him with the flat of his saber. Only a quick duck had saved Haines.

He poured himself another drink and carried it outside. He stared toward the south, and the sky-reflected fire cast an eerie light over the town. Let the goddam town burn up. He didn't care.

Still, it might be best to have his horse ready if he had to make a quick dash across the river. Yes, that would be the course of wisdom. But before he saddled he would go back into the tavern. This time he would take a bottle with him.

He took a step, and a terrible voice yelled, "Haines." He whirled and was sure his trembling legs were going to dump him into the street. A horseman galloped madly down the street toward him.

Fear held him in its awful trance until the horse was almost upon him. He didn't have to see the face to know who the rider was. Why Dryden didn't shoot, Haines didn't know. At any second he expected to see a tongue of flame lick out at him and feel the cruel, smashing impact of the bullet.

The horse was only a dozen feet from him before he was able to break that trance. A hoarse cry rattled in his throat, and he lunged to one side. He struggled to free the small pistol in his pocket. The pistol was a poor weapon to stop an onrushing horse, and he wished he had a rifle. The pistol caught in the pocket's lining, and he jerked at it. Sobs kept welling up into his throat, choking him.

The moment Eli saw the man step out into the street, he knew who it was. He kicked the horse into a full run, and the thud of its hoofs slammed in rolling echoes across the street. He carried his rifle in his right hand, but he didn't think of using it. All he wanted was to get close, to make physical contact.

"Haines," he roared.

Haines whirled, and Eli saw him lurch. The man seemed unable to move, and that suited Eli. He would run his horse through him. At the last split-second, Haines jumped to one side, and Eli couldn't swerve his horse quickly enough. The animal's shoulder grazed Haines, knocking him into a spinning, staggering run.

Eli wheeled his horse, and he was afraid Haines would escape into one of the buildings. He completed the tight turn and saw that the grazing impact had finally knocked Haines off his feet. Haines was just now scrambling to his knees. His hand raised from his waist, and the light reflected from something metallic.

The sight of the weapon had no braking effect on Eli's intentions. His mind was filled with the memory of Conley's broken face. He thundered back, and he could have ridden over Haines. But that would be ending it too quickly, that would cut Haines's suffering short. For Haines was suffering. It showed in his rigid face and in his open, screaming mouth.

Eli swerved at the last instant. He jerked a boot from its stirrup and kicked at Haines's face. His toe thudded into flesh, and he knew a fierce, primeval satisfaction.

He spun his horse, and Haines was on his back. He waited until Haines climbed painfully to his feet. Haines waved and reeled in the street, his head hanging low. His face was a ruin, the blood showing blackly against the white skin. He held both hands out in some imploring entreaty.

Eli drove the horse forward and kept it rigidly on course. It snorted as it smashed into Haines. The horse stumbled and went to its knees, and Eli jerked its head up. It regained its balance and raced on. Eli felt the slam of the hoofs into something soft and yielding. He turned it at the end of the block.

Haines looked like a bundle of old clothes dropped carelessly in the street. Eli walked his horse to him and looked down. Haines was dead. Eli panted like a man after a hard race. The vicious struggle couldn't have lasted more than a few seconds, but he felt completely drained and infinitely old.

CHAPTER TWENTY-THREE

Governor Samuel Medary was staring out the window as Walker entered the room. It looked like a peaceful land, but there were still dark undercurrents of hatred and violence. He was the sixth man to try his hand at governing Kansas Territory, and he had already experienced some of the frustrations and despair that must have driven his predecessors from office. But he could congratulate himself that things were improving. John Brown had left the territory, and Lane's whereabouts were unknown. Leaders of both factions were dropping out of sight, and no new ones were appearing to take their places. Perhaps men were becoming satiated with bloodletting, and perhaps his own efforts were having their effect. But whatever it was, law was here, and the individual was beginning to recognize it. The territory was well on its way to becoming a state.

He wheeled his chair around and looked at the badge pinned to Walker's shirt. Walker was a good man. He performed his official duties impartially, regardless of where his sympathies lay.

He asked, "Do you know Eli Dryden?"

"Yes, sir." Walker felt a stab of apprehension. Once he pinned on this badge, he knew he could put no friend ahead of the office. He guessed he had known that one of these days he would be sent to bring Eli in.

"I've issued a warrant for him. I want you to take a posse and go down and arrest him."

"Why?"

Medary looked astounded. "After the crimes he's committed you ask why?"

"We haven't enough jails in Kansas to hold all the men who have committed crimes, sir. I can give you a list longer than your arm." A rueful expression touched his face. "My name could very well be on that list."

Medary admitted that Walker was right. But there was a difference between that long list Walker spoke about and Eli Dryden. Dryden was still at it, where the others had faded quietly back into more or less respectable lives.

He pointed out that difference to Walker. "He'll never stop. He's been at it too long. Whenever something offends him, he'll take the law into his own hand. He'll keep that south country in constant ferment."

Walker looked unconvinced, and Medary asked, "You want more reasons? He's killed army horses. He rode into Fort Scott and burned it out. He killed a man there. The army is screaming for his scalp. As territorial governor they demand I act, or they will."

"He killed those horses defending himself, sir. I heard the town was saved. That dead man was trampled by a horse. It could have been a runaway horse, frightened by the fire."

"Do you believe what you just said?" Temper was showing in Medary's eyes. "Colonel Belmont's report listed an eyewitness who saw the man ridden down by a horseman."

"I don't believe what I just said, sir," Walker said quietly.

The governor's tone rose a pitch. "Then what are you arguing about?"

"The dead man was Ross Haines, sir. The man who ordered and participated in the Marais des Cygnes massacre. He killed eight men there, eight of Eli's best friends."

Medary tapped his teeth with a forefinger. Belmont's report hadn't included the dead man's name. Was it an oversight, or a willful omission? Outrage had been between every line of the report. When it came to protecting itself from humiliation, the army was suspect. Still, it was murder, no matter how much Walker tried to justify Dryden.

"You think it was Dryden, too, don't you?"

A fleeting smile touched Walker's face. "I never said that. It might have been Eli. If it was, he had his provocation."

Medary's face was severe. "And that makes it right for him to be his own court, judge and hangman?"

"No, sir, it does not."

"You admit that as long as Eli Dryden can influence other men to follow him he's dangerous to the whole structure of law and order?"

Walker nodded.

"Then what are we talking about? I want him brought in." A frown set his face. The stubbornness remained in Walker's face. He said testily, "You don't expect a pardon for him, do you?"

"He's worth saving," Walker said slowly. "Kansas needs men like Eli Dryden. Men with vision and the will to work to make that vision come true. I knew him when he first arrived here. His one intention was to get his land and work it. He thought that if a man minded his own business he would be left alone. He fought either side pulling him into their argument. His best friend was killed by Haines, and Haines burned his house. Eli saw there was no protection for any man unless he protected himself. I'm not denying he committed crimes. But every one of them was in retaliation against a crime committed against him or his friends."

"And that justifies what he did?"

"It doesn't," Walker said doggedly. "But he had his reasons."

"Every criminal can say that. You think after years of doing as he pleased he can change back into that peaceful man you talked about?"

Walker's face was troubled. "I don't know, sir."

Medary made a tepee of his fingers and stared at the ceiling.

Walker wished he could read the governor's thoughts. He had given every reason that could help Eli, and he had said it the best he could. He could do nothing more.

Medary picked up a folded paper from his desk top. "Pick your posse and serve this warrant."

"I'll go alone," Walker said woodenly. He had lost. "He'll

fight a body of men without asking questions. Experience has trained him that way."

"And you want to give him every chance," Medary said. He felt suddenly lonely and wistful. Men in high places had very few friends they could trust as Walker trusted Dryden. "You could be risking your life," he pointed out.

"Yes," Walker said.

"All right," Medary sighed. "Bring him in. I want to talk to this man. I want to see for myself that your judgment is as sound as you think. If he submits peacefully to arrest—well, we'll see."

Joy shone from Walker's eyes. He leaned across the desk and thrust out a hard hand. "Thank you, sir."

"I'm promising nothing," Medary warned. "I have every doubt in the world about this man. Right now, it's a matter of arresting Eli Dryden and bringing him here."

"Yes, sir," Walker said. He turned and marched out of the office.

Eli was coming out of Brady's tavern when he saw Walker ride down the street. He started to spring forward to greet him, then halted, his face going still. Was Walker here on official business?

Walker dismounted and turned a sober face toward Eli. He said, "Eli, I've got a warrant for your arrest."

Eli's face molded into a hard mask. "Ride out, Sam, while you're able."

"You're going with me," Walker said quietly.

Anger built in Eli's eyes. "You ride in here alone and tell me something like that. I never took you for a crazy man before."

"You're going back with me," Walker insisted.

Their stiff attitudes drew attention, and men drifted to the scene. Walker was surrounded by hostile faces.

"What is it, Eli," one of them asked.

"He came down to arrest me."

"By himself?" the man asked incredulously. Laughter broke

out among them. "What kind of marshals are they hiring these days?"

"You'd better leave while you can, Sam," Eli said.

"Not without you." Walker prayed silently, Eli, come with me. This could be the most important moment of your life.

"Don't make me kill you, Sam." Eli's eyes were deadly.

"Hell, we'll take care of it for you, Eli," Moran said.

"Stay out of this," Eli ordered. His eyes never left Walker.

"You might kill me," Walker admitted. He was sick with his defeat. "But they'll send others down after me. Can you kill them all?"

Eli's face was grim. "I can try. Your move, Sam."

"I think I'll just wait for you, Eli."

The moment trembled on a razor's edge. A wrong expression or even a breath could set it off. All the useless words had been said. Now each of them waited for movement from the other.

"Eli!" The voice was almost a scream. "Eli, stop that."

Lacey ran down the street, and her face was frantic. She pushed through the ring, and Eli scowled at her. "Lacey, get out of here."

Some purpose set her face. She walked between Eli and Walker and stopped. "Were you going to fight him?"

Eli's voice was ragged. "He forced me into it. I gave him every chance to leave." An unconscious entreaty crept into his voice. "He came down to arrest me, Lacey."

The plea didn't touch her. "And killing him would stop everything? You used to talk about him to me. You called him a friend."

The accusation in her eyes raked him. "He turned against me. All I asked was to be left alone."

Her eyes blazed at him. "You've hidden behind that for a long time, haven't you? How many times have you told me it was a job you had to do? Maybe he feels the same way about his job. Oh Eli, can't you see? It stops here, or it never stops. If you kill him, they'll only send others."

"I told him that," Walker murmured.

Lacey cried, "Do you want to be killed, or spend the rest of your life running?"

She saw no melting in his face. "Then go ahead," she said dully. "Shoot him. Then you might as well shoot me. Because every dream, every hope I had is already dead."

She turned, and Eli sprang forward and seized her shoulder. He wanted to cry at the deep anguish in her eyes. What a loss if those eyes never sparkled again. He said, "Lacey, try to understand."

"I do." Her eyes were dead. "I used to cry at night over Cass, over the terror and the suffering. But the hope that things would get better made it bearable. Now there's no more hope."

She had erected a wall against him, and he would never get through it. "I could be hanged, Lacey."

She flicked her eyes to Walker, and he said, "He might." A wry expression crossed his face. "Though I don't think so. We haven't enough hangmen to hang all the men in Kansas who've earned it. No, he'll get a fair hearing, with all the extenuating circumstances brought out."

"I could go to prison," Eli said bitterly. "Do you want that?"

She stared at him, and something breathed a remnant of hope into her eyes. "I'd wait," she said simply.

Walker's throat was tight as he watched them. This girl could turn Eli or nobody could.

Eli raised a hand to touch her, then dropped it. This was Lacey, this was his dream and his life. In her two simple words she had offered him everything.

He looked at Walker. "What about the men who rode with me?"

The listening men caught the weakening in Eli's question and howled their protests. He waved them quiet and asked, "Sam?"

Walker said steadily, "I can promise you that none of them are on any wanted list. If they stop, they won't be."

The protests continued, and Eli said savagely, "He's giving

you back your land, your families." He glared from one face to another. "Put down your rifles. That's my last order."

He shook his head. He had never expected to be saying words like those. Maybe with men like Sam Walker in office they wouldn't have to fight to protect themselves. He pulled the pistol from his belt and handed it to Walker. "I'm ready, Sam. Any time you are."

Tears streamed down Lacey's face, but they didn't rack him as that anguished hopelessness had, for there was no despair in these tears. He folded her in his arms and said, "I'll be back."

He tipped up her chin and wiped at the tears with a thumb. "I know that," she said. "Help him, Mr. Walker."

Walker said gravely, "I'll do everything I can."

Eli kissed her, then pushed her back. He looked from face to face. Something had touched them all, for the rebellion was gone.

He saddled and mounted, then rode out of town with Walker. He looked back, and his face was perplexed. "I must have been crazy to listen to you—or to her."

The old, easy grin was back on Walker's face. "No, you replaced one value with another."

They rode a couple of miles in silence before Eli said, "What's going to happen, Sam?" There might have been a touch of fear in his voice.

"Why we'll ride in and talk to the governor. I've found him a reasonable man. He'll listen to your side. He's more interested in stopping the trouble than in punishing for the past. You've submitted to arrest. I think he'll take it as proof you're ready to recognize law and order. I can't promise a thing, Eli. But I'd almost bet Medary will ask the legislature for amnesty for you. Maybe a token fine."

Eli's eyes shone with a joy that was almost painful to see.

Walker thought, A lot of burden just dropped from his back. And with it the toughness. Eli didn't look a day older than the young man Walker had met in Wakarusa.

He lifted the reins. "You ready to ride?"

Eli answered him steadily, "I'm ready to ride."

F51